Life, Death & Whisky.

(The Undertakers Stash)

By

Ralfy

Published in 2022

ISBN: 978-1-9162575-5-9

All characters, locations and places in this book are fictitious and there is no attempt intended to misrepresent any individual or organisation known, or unknown, to the author.

Warning – If you choose to drink alcohol and are of legal age to do so in your Country of residence, drink in moderation, with consideration, and know your healthy limits for the sake of yourself and those around you. Some content of this book may be distressing and upsetting, so please read with caution If you are at all sensitive about the subject of death, or have experienced a recent bereavement.

Edited by Helen Kaneen

ALSO BY RALFY -

Search For a Whisky Bothy

Stories From A Whisky Bar

Published by the Irish Sea Trading Company Ltd: ©

Ramsey, Isle Of Man, IM7 1HG, British Isles

® First Edition, Printed 2022

This book is dedicated

to malt-mates

and Pat=Pals.

Contents

Prologue.

Life, death and whisky, they have rather a lot of connection, something I have become more mindful of over the years.

Life? . . . is something that I am still quite happy to experience, as I am one of the lucky ones, having decent health, time to enjoy the experiences, and enough money not to suffer unduly, from deprivation and stress.

I live in a society which does not threaten me with violence, so long as I stay smart.

Death? . . . can wait, hopefully until I am ready.

Whisky? . . . well this is another contributor to life and death, a little amount being of tonic effect.

Too much will hastening death sooner, rather than later.

I was once ask if, as an undertaker, was I afraid of death?

"Only if I have not finished living yet," I replied.

Lets raise a glass to that.

Chapter One - Life, Death and Whisky

What's it all about?

Life, death, and whisky!

…with life, there is the experience of the event over a short period of time which concludes in death, obviously defined by the cessation of mortal life. Please note that I am saying 'mortal' life as there is increasing evidence from scientific sources, and wiser philosophies, that life exists before birth and after death when we are talking about present mortality references. This applies to all living things.

I know, controversial already and I am only one hundred and fifty-one words into this book.

Death (through the circumstance of the food we have to eat) allows for the sustaining of life, so one without the other is impossible in this dimension. Life needs death and death needs life, and whilst the two are essentially inseparable, life concludes with death which can only be preceded by life.

Life and death, for us, are two conjoining dancers, twisting and turning and making predictable moves, each meaningless without the reference caused by one another's presence.

Then there is the whisky, confusing things as always, and making us think unconventional thoughts in our transition from being sober to non-sober. It's that alcohol thing. My experience is that a sober contemplation of life and death is less illustrative and insightful compared to thoughts under the influence of alcohol, probably because the wisdom of natural instincts kick in after a few drams of liquor, and inhibitions are less censoring.

I'm probably feeling a little life-and-death focused at the moment as one of my neighbours down the stairs in the tenement has just died, and was found by her daughter in the morning, still and cold in her bed. She was eighty-five years old and had led a simple, humble and routine life keeping herself to herself. I'm thinking that her departure is the right way to go, quietly, peacefully, alone and without fuss and frenzy. It has dignity.

I am snapped away from my thoughts by a gentle knock on my front door. Judging by the steady, polite knocks, it must be my next-door neighbour down stairs, Margaret.

She is a lovely, old-fashioned, and single lady who has chosen her path in life to be quiet and filled with friends rather than family. In fact, her friends are her family, and she is all the better for this situation.

Margaret is in her early seventies, prim, observant and well-intentioned, small, slight and well dressed, with short curly hair dyed a slight tinge of smoky lavender, and she smells discreetly of Chanel No 5. With her not having a family, her secretary job has allowed for some well-placed luxuries over the years. She is quite a character.

"Oh! Ralf, I'm glad I got you in dear," she chimes, arms folded, and offering a genuine smile. "That's wee Mrs Maclure passed away peacefully last night, and the undertakers have just taken her to Robertsons parlour down in Hayburn Street, where you can pop in tomorrow to view her and pay your respects," she pauses for my reaction, ". . . if you really want to," she adds, assessing my expression as a much younger man, who in her eyes, is more naive and probably squeamish about such things.

"Thanks Margaret for letting me know, but I think I will give it a miss as I never really saw much of her, what with only moving into the close less than a year ago, but," I add, "I will sort out a wee bunch of flowers, if you can pass them onto the family for me."

"Well, actually," replies Margaret, "I'm organising a collection around the close to get something for us all, as she lived here for over sixty years you know, since about, um, well . . . nineteen twenty, twney-eight, . . . yes, that's when she moved in."

"How much do you want to give, say about five pounds, and with nine of us in the tenement, we can get a larger forty pound bouquet with seasonal flowers along with a box of biscuits."

And then she adds, "But I know you're not working at the moment so money might be tight, so a couple of quid will do if you're struggling!"

I thank Margaret for her consideration, and hand over a five pound note. I also confirm that out of civility, I will visit Mrs Maclure at Robertsons' the following afternoon after my job interview in the morning.

The interview is awful, 'catering manager' at a dismal old mansion house on the outskirts of Glasgow, now functioning as a centre for children with behavioural problems. Everything is miserable, including the featureless woman who interviews me, then makes it clear at the conclusion of the ten minute interview that I am the 'wrong sort' and wishes me luck in finding something suitable.

Four interviews in five weeks, all catering, and all just rotten jobs offering lousy pay. It is now three months since I have been made redundant along with sixteen other staff from the restaurant I have managed for two years in the City centre. It has been a demanding and exhausting job, not helped by the lack of investment by the owners, both of their cash, of which they had plenty, and of their time, which is not spent on looking after their businesses. They received an offer for the premises which they decided to accept, despite the business making profits for the first time in years. I am now down to the last hundred pounds of my redundancy payment, and still looking for a job.

I visited my bank up in Byres Road who was providing the mortgage on my flat, and explained that I might not be able to make the next payment. The manager made a note of my circumstances and then quickly showed me to the door, saying, "We can do something when you have no money."

Can I tell you something about banks and mortgage lenders?

They, in my opinion, engage in fraud and theft from naive customers who make the mistake of trusting institutions of 'authority'. On both occasions that I bought a property, I was charged for 'bridging loans' despite the properties being unoccupied on both occasions, and payment exchanges did not require these loans.

I was young, naive, and just wanted to have somewhere to call my own, so I never challenged the fraud as it could have cancelled the purchases, but I did make a note then to acknowledge that society sanctions exploitation and state-fraud to a degree I was never told about in school.

School never prepares us for the real world. School is there to indoctrinate and subjugate the masses. To create obedient workers who can write clearly and do arithmetic at a basic level, then work for as little money as tolerable.

Mrs Maclure looks reposed, pale and cold, laying peacefully in her simple, light-coloured coffin. Her mouth seems closed too tight, making her lips purse up slightly in an angry sort of way. Her eyes are closed, nearly, but not quite. She is wearing a white nylon, ornamental shroud which matches the thin frilly lining round the top of the coffin.

I have arrived late in the day, long after family have viewed, and then concluded the final details of the funeral arrangement with the lady who looks after the Parlour. I am ushered into a wood panelled room in silence and then immediately left to pay my respects.

The room is tiny, sparse, basic, with brown-stained plywood surfaces, and a drab single source lighting. A locked double door leads directly out onto Hayburn Street so that is easier to load the hearse should a service be taking place within the small chapel inside which can hold up to twenty people at a push. It's very calm and detached from the animated world outside, feeling like a 'separate' sort of place, untouched by daily reality.

I pause to examine the grey-ness of Mrs Maclure's colour when the door slides open, and Margaret pops her head in respectfully to announce her presence. "She's looking peaceful, isn't she?" she states calmly, drawing out the small bottle of Chanel No5 from her coat pocket. She sprays a little of the perfume over the deceased, and whilst the complex floral odour lift upwards towards my nose, she explains that the family had requested that she do so. It seems fitting.

"Will you be leaving some of your fancy single malt whisky in the coffin then?" she asks humorously. "Well," I respond, "I had not actually thought about that, do you think she would appreciate, well, er . . . have appreciated the gesture?"

"Probably not" responds Margaret, giggling, "She hated the smell of the stuff."

We settle into our seats at the Tea Garden Cafe in Gardner Street and order tea and scones. I offer to pay, but Margaret insists that she pays, so I let her. She has her reasons. "How's the job-hunting going?" she asks diplomatically. I mumble some polite response about "something will be just round the corner", and she goes silent for a moment in sympathy for my situation. "I've had about nine job interviews now," I continue, to break the growing awkwardness, and Margaret breezily changes the subject to whisky, a subject that she knows I will be more comfortable with as we sip our cooling tea, and nibble on the toasted teacakes, now cold, but still appetising and appreciated. Really, the first treat in about three months, apart from the drams I take from my stash of bottles stored discreetly in a spare cupboard in the flat.

Someone has left a newspaper on the table next to us, neatly folded, and looking fresh out of the newsagents. She flicks through methodically, skipping the main news items, which are of no interest to us, and suddenly stops near the back, jabbing a manicured finger towards the top of the page. "Look!" she states, "A wee jobs section of adverts left over from Wednesday's edition."

She pauses, squints, then thrusts the now folded paper towards me pointing at a small ad in the corner, simple and unambiguous:

Co-operative Funeral Care

Trainee Funeral Director

No experience required

Contact phone number below

for application form.

Margaret laughs nervously, "How about this one then," she states, "You now know a bit more than yesterday about funerals, and I think you've got the patience and tact for it."

I stare at the ad, and think, well, there's nothing to lose, an interview is an interview, if it happens.

It does.

My interview is the following Friday in Paisley Road, at the main Glasgow Office of Co-operative Funeralcare. The interview is at 2.30pm, and I better not be late.

The night before, I get a little nervous, after-all, it's not a job many people would want to do, what with upset families and dead bodies, but I really need a job or I will lose my flat, and my stash of whisky too. I pour a large glass of single malt, followed by another, then, finally, after an hour or so, another just to help me sleep, but the night is restless and troubled, with crashing hearses and dropped coffins, and angry, spiteful families.

The underground train rattles and rocks its way from Kelvin Hall in Partick to West Street on the south-side, passing through Glasgow City centre on the way, bustling with rushing bored shoppers and late morning commuters. I alight at West Street to sunshine, a mild refreshing breeze, and a sudden, unexpected feeling of relief as the anxiety of the night before finally dissipates and leaves me feeling calmer and less wound-up about the forthcoming interview.

On arrival at 119 Paisley Road, Head Quarters of The Co-operative Funeral Service, I am ushered at reception, almost immediately, by a tall and gangly lady towards a near-by reception room in which two men are sitting, one behind a desk, and the second, on an uncomfortable looking seat immediately behind the door.

Mr Roy is smaller, kinder, and the quiet one, with little to contribute or say, whilst Mr Dick commands the room behind his imposing, and largely empty desk, save for a few pencils in a plastic holder and a note pad.

Mr Dick is a small, dull, puffy-looking man, hiding behind a thick, bushy beard, and speaking in a contrived regional accent, designed, and articulated to express his self-confidence and authority. He looks like a politician or a civil-servant from a department of less importance. He is officious from the very start.

"Hello then," he states breezily, not even acknowledging my name. "My name is Mr Dick, and I am the Operations Manager." He concludes, re-directing his attention to a folder now thrown onto the desk top with a slapping sound. He then lets the silence hang for a at least a minute whilst he studies my completed application form, stapled to some typewritten attached notes on a plain sheet of white paper.

"You've had some adventures then?" he states, looking up briefly, then just as quickly, he moves onto his set questions. He is not interested in an answer to that question.

What are your goals and ambitions?

Where do you see yourself in five years?

Are you good with tight-schedules and 'pressure' situations?

Do you have a full and clean driving licence?

I answer politely and carefully, keeping answers short and light.

Strangely, I don't feel any anxiety, or sense of being under pressure. It all seems like a dispassionate formality and a box-ticking exercise. There is no real interview as such, at least not that I had expected.

Mr Dick concludes with one final question.

"How do you think you will cope with dead human bodies?"

"Some of them will be in a very distressing condition you know!"

I pause, reflecting consciously upon his significant question, then start by narrating my viewing of Mrs Maclure at Robertsons' Parlour in Hayburn Street, two days before, and conclude with an incident I had a number of years previously in Panama, where I had to help bury a dead body left by a road side.

Mr Dick, for the first time seems impressed and even Mr Roy, sitting quietly in the corner pipes up with a compliment about my decency in the situation. Mr Dick casts his subordinate a dirty look for daring to interrupt proceedings.

"After all," I conclude, "There is no dignity in death, except for the dignity that the living can offer to the deceased."

Mr Dick glances quickly across the table, seeming genuinely interested in me for the first time over the fifteen minute interview.

9

As his colleague Mr Roy escorts me to the front door, he confides, kindly and sincerely, that I have given a good interview, and will be hearing from the Co-operative personnel department with the results in the next two weeks. I receive a phone call on the following Monday afternoon from Mr Dick himself. "When can you start?" he asks abruptly. "As soon as you want me to." I reply.

As soon as I hang up the phone, I feel the weight of the last three months unemployment lift suddenly from my shoulders. I am working again, making my way, doing something. I don't even think about what it will be. For now it just does not matter. I pour a wee dram of single malt, and shut my eyes as the amber liquor coats my tongue.

That night, after a visit to my local bar, the Smiddy, down on Dumbarton Road, I return home to a dinner of beans on toast, as this is really all I have left in the cupboard, and after the modest meal, I get gently drunk on whisky, but not too much, even though I have plenty of it. I have not yet told them in the pub about my new job in anticipation of a weird reaction, or worse, being dismissed as a 'creepy ghoul'.

I am sitting in the flat, first thing on a Sunday morning, sipping tea, with the fresh winter light streaming through the windows, as the early December sun blinks a little warmth into the small room, and I sense the profound relief that I will now be able to make my next mortgage payment. I am starting a new job tomorrow, so I look out my plain grey suit, polish my black leather Doc Martins, and iron the only white shirt that I have hanging in the wardrobe.

When the good folks and regulars at the Smiddy hear about my new career, they laugh themselves silly.

"Do you test the coffins for comfort?" asked Izzy, a cheery, round wee woman who works at the Shieldhall bottling plant, bottling Johnnie Walker.

"Do you get special training to be a miserable creepy bastard?" asked Sanny, the retired Cooper.

"Do the bodies move around and sit up in the coffins when you're not looking?" enquires James the barman, grinning as he slowly wipes his beer glasses dry behind the bar.

I take it all in good humour, and assure them all that I will be happy to supply estimates and quotes on costs, should it be required . . . and after I have been properly trained. Everyone finds it hilarious at the Smiddy, and when Janice, a local florist who is also a regular there spontaneously offers to give me a tour round her wee shop along the road, the venue erupts with sustained and prolonged laughter.

Later on I pop down stairs to let Margaret know of the situation, but she is out at a church social, so I will have to catch up with her later.

Back in my flat, time is getting on so I pour a wee glass of a blended whisky, donated at my front door, and for free, as part of a marketing exercise hosted by the owners of the Bells brand. It's called Bell's Islander, and is basically standard Bell's with a bit of Islay peatiness in it for some added depth and 'kick'. I drink it neat.

It's the 1980s so any whisky initiative is going to help because sales are sluggish, primarily due to vodka still being the spirit of choice, whilst whisky is an 'old man's drink'. Distilleries are shutting, closing down, being 'mothballed' and staff are being made redundant, just like myself a few months previously, we share a common fate. I hope they find a job too. The 'unemployment' threat has always been a useful weapon invested in by those with power to keep the masses fearful and in-line.

The blend is fine, if a little simple and anaemic, so I pour a single malt next, as a reward for recent achievement. Bunnahabhain 12yo, 'Westering Home' is says on the label. The liquor is only 40% by volume of alcohol, but, there's more 'nose' more 'bite' more 'flavour' and more substance than is found in the smell and taste of the Bell's blend. Already, I prefer malts to blends, they always offer more character, despite some blends showing good flavour balance and methodical maturation from decent casks. Malts offer more, but, of course, it goes both ways, and if the malt is good, the goodness is articulated better, but, if the malt is bad, that is articulated too.

As I contemplate the complexity of the Bunnahabhain experience, I hear the footsteps of Margaret returning from her church-social, and trot down to the landing below to let her know the news. I take what's left of the Bell's Islander, and offer it to her as a gift. She always has ginger ale in her whisky, so there's no point in giving her some malt. It would not be appreciated. Standing at her door, we briefly discuss life, churches, whisky and funerals. "It was supposed to happen I suppose," she suggests. "What with Mrs Maclures funeral viewing and such and finding that newspaper just sitting on the next table at the Tea Garden!"

I nod sagely, "And you Margaret, being in the right place at the right time, doing the right thing". She thinks deeply for a few seconds, and then agrees. I head back upstairs feeling that I was a bit mean just giving her a half empty bottle of blend as a gift. But she liked it anyway. "Bell's is good stuff," she declared knowingly, "It goes perfect with ginger ale."

I head off early for my first day of work at a new job on Monday the 5th of December 1988. It is raining, cold, and the subway is full of people coughing and sneezing, wiping noses and looking washed-out. I shiver briefly at the thought that I am now looking at my fellow commuters as potential customers. Is it normal for an undertaker to think this way?

The subway carriage arrives, rattling and rocking into West Street, and I alight to the breeze of a fresh, dry and remarkably mild day, just as the short winter daylight begins. It is 8.15am, I am due to start at 8.30am and I must be sure not to be late, as undertakers are very punctual people who hate being late, especially at the church for a service, or at the crematorium for a committal.

After a refreshingly short walk I enter the front door on Paisley Road, Glasgow, of the Co-operative Funeral Service. Entering through two metal-framed glass doors, a reception desk appears directly across on my right hand side. I walk over and introduce myself to the young, tall, pleasant-looking lady who looks up slightly startled and asks me, "Are you here to view or make arrangements?"

I pause, caught by surprise at this unexpected misunderstanding. "No, actually, I'm Ralph Mitchell . . . and I'm starting work here today!" It's the lady's turn to look surprised. She continues, ". . . well, nobody's said anything to me . . . are you sure you have the right place?"

I pause for a moment wondering if in fact I do have the right place, then add, "Mr Dick phoned me last week to say I had a job as a trainee undertaker." "Ah well!" responds the tall and pleasant lady, "nobody told me anything about it, as usual, typical, there's never any communication round this place . . . well you better take a seat whilst I find someone to deal with you."

I take a seat, and after about ten minutes, a very portly, greasy-looking man appears and whilst grinning, and rubbing his podgy hands together, introduces himself as the shift manager, John Farrell. "We don't have a uniform for you, or anything else for that matter, but you can sit in the office and watch what we're doing for an hour until we find you something else to do". He simpers, affecting cartoonish civility and an odd air of amateurism. Once in the office, he abruptly leaves me on a chair in the corner and promptly disappears.

I sit and wait, watching two rather tired, dark-clad funeral directors answer calls and then spend up to twenty minutes at a time, hand-writing in pencil, individual arrangement details given over the phone by parlour receptionist, thereafter transposing the taken details onto a four-section job sheet with a top white copy, a yellow copy, a pink copy and a blue copy, one for each processing department. The white copy stays in the office, the yellow goes to the coffin furnishing workshop, the pink copy to the embalmers, and finally the blue copy to the transport garage up the road in Scotland Street. I wonder to myself as to why this process is not automated, at least with a fax machine, which would speed things up considerably.

Both stale and fresh cigarette smoke permeates the air and several phones ring regularly, remaining unanswered, whilst the two staff members remain heads-down taking details and asking questions, writing in pencil, and just doing their job.

Time goes on slowly, and I am sitting feeling useless. I indicate to one of the funeral directors as to whether I should answer the next phone when it rings. He nods his head in a 'no' and says, "Let it ring mate, there should be another body in this place to help out, but everyone's out on jobs at the moment.". He coughs violently, turning red in the face, then lights another cigarette. I settle back onto my seat as another phone begins to ring yet again. The receptionist passes by on her way to make a cup of coffee, and phones now ring at reception, but for a few minutes are left unanswered.

After fifteen minutes of feeling awkward and useless, a tall, gaunt greying man enters the office wearing a dark blue anorak, and carrying a black folder stuffed with work sheets and assorted papers, and gives me a friendly, inquisitive smile.

"You the new guy then?" he asks.

"Yes!" I reply.

"What are you doing then?" he continues.

"Nothing at the moment!" I respond.

He sighs, nodding his head, "Typical round here!" He pauses to consider the situation further, then heads off down the corridor and briefly into the shift manager's office, which has its door firmly closed against interruptions. Following his brief interruption, I am assigned my first job, to accompany, and help him on the van.

"I'm Alec," he tells me as way of introduction as we speed off in a tatty black transit van, modified to carry coffins, flowers, trestles, trolleys, and anything else that needs carried, and is dignified to do so.

As we amble down Paisley Road and over the bridge onto the Broomielaw, Alec lights a cigarette and offers me one, which I accept courteously. With the van windows down, to release the fog of tobacco accumulating in the vehicle, Alec offers some advice. "There's three van drivers on the team, myself, wee Norrie, and Hugh. Norrie's a right wee sweetie-wife, and just wants to get on with what he wants to do, and Hugh, we call him Shuggie, doesn't say much, so you won't get much out of him, he's a miserable big cunt!"

He turns to check my reaction. I remain impassive.

We draw up to a red traffic light as we turn from the Bridgegate into Crown Street, down at the bottom of the Saltmarket. Alec turns to look at me, checking my reaction. "We're going to the City Mortuary at Jocelyn Square, just round the corner," he pauses, continuing to check my reaction, "you may find that there is a bit of a smell about the place."

The van swings round the corner and towards a compact blond sandstone and red brick art deco building, discreetly imposing and with restrained character. Around the back of the building is a small, walled courtyard, fenced by two large double wooden gates, painted brown to avoid public attention. As soon as the van is reversed into the compound, I am instructed to close both gates, and ensure the large iron bolt is drawn over to secure the gates and stop any peeping-toms, or nosey by-passers from peeking in to see the 'bodies'. It has happened in the past, several times.

Alec alights from the van, now reversed neatly to the bottom of a short flight of concrete steps leading up to an open double door, where a cheery weather-beaten man stands grinning, sleeves rolled up and holding a dirty ceramic mug with what looks like hot tea in it, judging by the small spiral of raising steam ascending from the container. Raggedy, greyish and scrawny, he seems to be oblivious to what the world thinks of him and his job, and therefore just does not care.

"That you got a new one for me Alec?" he chortles, thereafter, sipping noisily from his mug.

Alec sighs, "Ay! Jackie, a new one just started today."

"Well, you won't want to be wearing your nice suit at a wedding now, will you?" he laughs.

"Not after you've been handling bodies at the Cities Mortuary."

Alec just nods his head, and gestures me into the mortuary, where a large terrazzo tiled room houses a line of fridges, along with a hoist trolley

15

and several sets of trestles. "Don't you listen to him now," he advises, "Jackie's just fine, but he is full of mischief."

Jackie appears into the room through swinging translucent plastic doors, which provide access to the post-mortem theatre the other side of the wall of fridges. Now he is wearing a plastic apron and a pair of disposable gloves. He raises the adjustable trolly to about four feet in height, opens a fridge door, and breezily pulls out a galvanised grey metal tray on which the naked body of a recently post mortemed old man lays silently, grey and cold. Jackie stands back, and both men now stare at me for several seconds registering my reaction.

I remain calm and impassive. I am unmoved.

"So, will you give me a hand to coffin him then?" asks Alec. I affirm that I will, and as Jackie arranges a couple of low trestles to place an empty coffin on, Alec and I return to the van to unload and carry into the mortuary, a simple, lightweight dark veneered coffin which Alec tells me is called a 'tiree'.

I pull a pair of disposable gloves from a box discarded in the passenger seat door space, and we carry the empty coffin up the stairs and into the room where the two of us gently place the deceased into the plastic lined chipboard coffin and after having secured the lid with four gold-coloured plastic-topped retaining screws, we carefully manage our way back out of the building and into the back of the van, securing the coffin with steel retaining pegs, with fat rubber washers designed to prevent damage to the coffins in transit.

"Jackie Stirling," says Alec, "is a good lad, and will always do his best to help you, unlike some others. There's a wee shit there called Nick, a horrible wee prick, so watch yourself with him". I heed Alec's advice carefully as we head up via the Trongate to the Glasgow Royal Infirmary. There, we collect three more bodies in their coffins by way of an old fashioned small antique lift which helps us avoid the necessity of going up and down stairs.

After we have unloaded all four coffins at the co-operative mortuary located in Laidlaw Street, just round the corner from the main entrance, we walk back around the viewing rooms to the office where I started in the morning, and hand over our four completed work-sheets to shift-leader John Farrell, who wheezers and blusters about his workload. Then, after some thought, instructs Alec to drive me up to the main garage in Scotland Street where I can see the coffins being made up with linings and sidesets. He just wants me out of his way, so not much in the way of introduction to the Co-op then! That will have to wait.

As we drive up the road to the Scotland Street garage, Alec turns to me, "Well then!" he asks, " . . . do you think you'll be back tomorrow, or was one day enough?"

"I'll be back tomorrow Alec, today was just fine, and thanks for helping me get to see some of the job, I appreciate it," I reply.

Chapter Two - The story of Mrs Hailstones, and pelters at the Smiddy.

...time passes fast when you're very busy.

I have been working at the Co-op now for over a month, and Christmas has been and gone.

It was rather weird, Christmas Day on duty at the undertakers. I was assured by my colleagues, that it's usually quiet on a Christmas Day because people don't want to die until after they have opened their presents, so they leave it till Boxing Day when it's not so important, or until they have discovered that the presents were not worth opening, and they have probably fallen-out with their family anyway . . . again.

This happens a lot, unwanted presents, arguing families, and other issues, which is why all the best presents are the ones we buy for ourselves, with our own money, and we should open them alone.

Five of us were sat round a table in the staff room, keeping one ear out for phones ringing at reception, and with a disposable paper 'jinglebells' tablecloth, cheap crackers, and microwave turkey lunch, washed down with ginger beer, it was all very jolly . . . within reason.

If the phone rang, which it didn't, we would suddenly become hushed so as to observe a background respect for a potentially bereaved caller, phoning on the worst day for such a bereavement to happen. The most interesting call had been a few days previous, when an angry young woman phoned to arrange a wreath to be delivered, by hearse, to her ex-boyfriend's address at a time that she knew him to be at home with his new girlfriend, on Christmas Eve. As a professional service provider, her request was politely declined. Being most upset at the response, she phoned the fire brigade instead, claiming her boyfriends garage was on fire.

I was working my first Christmas Day which was quiet, and as such, mutually agreed that the shift personnel of eight undertakers and two drivers would work split shifts of two halves, one half covering 8am to 2pm, and the other 2pm till 7pm, where after, the night shift team would take over. This slightly reduced the working day as it is for a legitimate reason. It was Christmas, season of peace and goodwill, and less work. A few vehicles were washed to help pass the time, and most folks talked about what they are having for dinner that night.

It is quite atmospheric in a Dickensian sort of way.

As I walked back home that afternoon, I thought intensely of people and the place in which I live, and had my own Christmas chicken dinner alone, with a small fruit dumpling dessert, and it was just perfect. All that I wanted, along with a few drams of single malt.

Discovering towards the end of my first month in new employment that my earnings are more than double that of my previous job does certainly add a cosy glow to the task of learning the trade. I am busy, very busy. It just never stops.

It is deemed necessary that I remain on the vans for the first few weeks of January 1989, attending to hospital and nursing home removals along with police sudden death call pick-ups for the local coroner, called the 'procurator fiscal', as the business is too busy to train me in conducting and arranging funerals. At this point, I get a Co-op-provided suit to wear, along with white shirts, black shoes, black socks, a black top hat and a drivers formal cap.

By February, the Co-op is busy enabling over 263 funerals to take place in one week due to an unexpected flu outbreak. 36 undertakers, 3 van drivers, 25 limousine drivers, 3 embalmers and 35 local parlour receptionists make it happen, along with hired-in contractors enabling up to 16 hearses and 33 limousines to facilitate over 65 funerals to take place in one single day. Nothing like it has ever been seen before. Some hearses conduct up to seven funerals in one single day. There was no other option. It just has to be done.

With the overtime involved, recorded neatly in small, red, hard-backed note books, I soon have more money to buy more whisky, so I do.

Early shifts are 8.30am to 4.30pm, with time taken where one can find it to have lunch and an occasional tea-break. Some days are easier for breaks than others and it is not unusual to have lunch at a crematorium whilst a committal service is taking place. Lunch is usually in the back of a vehicle and out of the way of public view.

Late shifts are 8.30am to 7.00pm or later, sometimes 9.30pm if a priest has a late church reception as part of a vigil. We also work 10 hours on a Saturday and 9 hours on a Sunday, every third weekend. Three shifts of twelve undertakers work an average of 50 hours a week on a rolling basis.

Sure, these are long hours, but the overtime is good, and it's normal for British culture where the manual class work long hours, whilst the educated class work an average of 40 hours a week, and for higher pay. It is normal and accepted. In fact, on discussion, it is actually agreed that it's better to work longer hours with a varied, interesting job, than shorter hours with a boring, pointless job. Many well-paid jobs in the modern world are pointless. It's real life.

I begin to notice that my lower back is getting more painful at times. It is not the heavy lifting of coffins that causes this so much as the twisting and turning whilst carrying any weight of coffin, onto and off the van, or a hearse, or a catafalque at a crematorium. Of course, the heavier the coffin, the more the discomfort. I start to consume cod liver oil in small quantities out of a bottle from the chemists, and this helps my joints.

Most of my new colleagues are supportive and helpful, offering advice and information to help me deal with the bewildering variety of hospitals, nursing homes, clinics, hospices and surgeries I need to be aware of. I buy an A-Z Road Map of the City and lay it out on my front room carpet, to begin learning the main trunk roads of Glasgow. I start by separating the city along the River Clyde, isolating the north side from the south side. Then I isolate main roads. In the north, Dumbarton Road, Great Western Road, Balmore Road, Springburn Road etc., like radial numbers around a wall clock. Gradually, over time, I remember more roads from memory rather than needing to look at a map book. There's an awful lot of information to learn.

Some of my new colleagues are not helpful, and either they are thick, ignorant, or worse, just plain spiteful and nasty. It's just who they are, so I keep out their way as best I can.

My shift manager John Farrell does not seem to like me much. I never find out why.

He is a short, obese and ingratiating man, oily in appearance, and with a simpering, oily voice, his infrequent response to calls coming into the office from the public are a hoot. Seriously, he once explained to a client on the phone that he could not send a hearse to the deceased's house within the hour as he 'Only Had a skeleton staff'.

He is very partial to going into his office with a microwaved garlic sausage, a large one, bought from the supermarket. Then he closes the door firmly, eats the sausage, ignoring any incoming calls, then arranges a fish and chip supper from a chip shop to consume on the way home in his car, where, on returning home, he will eat another dinner prepared by his wife. He once boasted that the 14lb turkey cooked for a family gathering, was consumed by himself and his wife over one day as they were stuck in the house with no family turning up for the dinner, and they did not want anything going to waste. The cat got some turkey too, eventually.

At one point, three months in to the job, John Farrell slides into Mr Dicks office and suggests that 'Ralf's just not working out with the job'. On further enquiry, Mr Dick finds out from several experienced members of staff that ralf is doing just fine, and getting to grips with the job no problem. Mr Dick seems to get a lot of poor advice from his management team on a regular basis.

I am taken off the van for a day to get more experience working in the office. After carefully completing six or so translations from a funeral arrangement form onto a four-part processing form, I get the results checked by the manager who happens to be in the office at the time. His name is Ronnie and he is arguably the most pleasant mannered of the three shift managers. He affirms that the details are all present and correct and that I have leaned hard enough with my pen for the impregnated ink in the forms to pass through to the bottom blue copy, clearly.

"Now will you take a car and go and arrange a funeral?" he says.

"Ronnie, I've not been shown how to do that yet, no training or nothing, as I have been on the van for most of the time," I respond. He grins, sheepishly, "Well it's not a real arrangement, just a collecting of basic information, so you will be fine, anyway, she's just an old dear who has been waiting a bit too long, and we have nobody else available to respond."

I think for a minute, then suggest, "How about I make provisional arrangements to be completed at the local parlour to where she lives, will that be ok?"

"Fine," he replies, "Now just go!"

"Here's the details," he hands over a small first-contact slip, standard issue, basic information

'Mrs Hailstones' it reads.

Flat 5-4, 12 Carbisdale Street,

Springburn.

I phone the number provided but there is no answer so I head out into the traffic anyway, and over the River Clyde to the address given.

I arrive fifteen minutes later outside a well-managed block of modern council flats, situated just up a bit from the Salvation Army Centre in Fernbank Street. I knock the door, but there is no answer, so I try phoning again, and just as I think the phone is ringing-out, a fragile voice answers "Hello!"

"Mrs Hailstones," I pause, gauging her situation, "I am just at your front door now, my name's Ralf Mitchell, and I am here to make arrangements for you." I listen to her shuffle down a hallway to answer her door, but it does not happen, so I knock the door. "Did you hear me knocking Mrs Hailstones?" I ask politely. "No!" she replies, "nobody is knocking the door". I am confused, I reckon we both are.

Suddenly, I think of something, "Mrs Hailstones, the address I have is flat 5, 4th floor of 12 Carbisdale Street, is this correct?"

"No son, that's my address, I'm at my husbands' address, number 53 Otago Street, Hillhead."

22

I arrive ten minutes later at the neat blond sandstone, traditional tenement nestled deep within the west end of the city, and climb the stairs to the first floor, where a tiny, fragile old woman greets me enthusiastically, beckoning me into the biggest room of the small flat, where some packed cardboard boxes sit, about six of them, next to an armchair which is looking the worse for wear and tear over the decades. The room is silent, calm and full of memories. Sunlight dimples the large bay window.

I place down my newly provided arrangement case, and unfold my arrangement pad, exposing a blank piece of paper on which to take the basic details.

"You see son," she suddenly blurts out, "Don't apologise for the long delay, even although I phoned last night down to the funeral parlour, because I'm grateful for having the extra time to just sit here and remember what was with the two of us, me and John . . . John Hailstones."

I sit back comfortably in a seat opposite her armchair, anticipating some personal drama, and making a point to listen carefully and attentively, rather than simply gather the needed information as quickly as possible. "We first met at a picture hall in town, just after the big war, and it was love at first sight."

She sighs, looking towards the large bay window, where winter sunlight dapples and sparkles. Spontaneously, she fingers a modest diamond ring with her right hand, turning it like a small wheel around her left-hand finger. She glances down towards it briefly, and then brings her attention back to me suddenly. "But we could not get married; our families would not allow it. I was catholic and John was protestant, so being together was out of the question for us, it was not acceptable then. In fact, I was put into an arranged marriage six weeks after we had met, with another man, a nice, considerate man, but not my John. And that was it, I never saw John again, but just had to carry on with life, bringing up a family, who finally then went their own ways, and then my husband died, suddenly, peacefully at home, but even then, when he asked me if I had grown over time to love him a little, I had to say no. It broke my heart, but he deserved the truth, so I told him the truth, even though it hurt him."

23

I pause, still in the calm of the room, mulling Mrs Hailstones confession, then allow her to continue, as her story is far from over. "After my husband died, I got a message from my family that John was dead too, so there was no point of trying to get in touch, even though times were changing for the better with social attitudes, so I move on, and got a wee flat in Carbisdale Street, out of the way, and was finally left alone to my own devices. It was quite nice, still is really," she pauses looking lost within her memories, detached and remote, with, it seems, every reason to be.

I wait patiently, pen in hand, ready to take arrangement details, and still listening attentively to my client. "Then four weeks ago, when I was in the city centre for an opticians appointment, I was just trying on my new glasses, and there, across the shop, getting fitted for his own spectacles, was John, my John, and even after sixty years we knew each other instantly. I just cried seeing him there, and he hugged me, and we went to a coffee shop, then he invited me to lunch."

"Oh!" exclaims Mrs Hailstones, tears welling up in her eyes, "It was so beautiful!"

A moments silence fills the sun lit room, and the old lady sobs a little to herself.

I give her a moment to get composed, and I continue to listen carefully.

"He bought me this!" she exclaims suddenly, thrusting her ring bearing finger to me.

The humble ring sparkles intensely with its honesty and purpose.

"For our engagement," she concludes.

"Then this!" She shows a wedding ring nestled next to the other.

"We got married in the hospice two days ago."

"And now, Mister Mitchell," she continues, "I have to arrange his funeral with you. He only told me last week that he had cancer, and was going into the hospice for a few days. That was four days ago, but I made sure to visit every day, even though it meant getting three different buses to get there. He died yesterday morning, and I was there with him till the last minute. He said he loves my dearly and will wait for me in heaven."

She begins to cry softly.

I give her a few minutes to let it pass.

We proceed gently with some basic arrangement details; her full name, relationship to the deceased, contact phone number, the full name and address of deceased, place of death, cremation or burial? It's all laid out clearly on a standard arrangement sheet so I just follow it carefully, being sure not to miss anything out.

"Officiating clergy?" I ask.

"Absolutely not," she responds abruptly.

"Flowers?" I ask.

"Just a wee spray of colourful white lilies," she responds.

"Limousine?" I ask.

"Just one for me and my two neighbours."

"Where will the limousine pick you up, and then return you to after the crematorium?" I ask

"Just at my flat, then back there after, nothing fancy, we're not going anywhere for a purvey."

"Would you like me to arrange a humanist to say a few words at the crematorium?" I ask.

"Yes, but nothing religious, I don't want any of that, not now." She affirms confidently.

"What coffin would you like for him?" I ask nervously, anticipating more tears. I show her pictures from my brochure which she views, one by one, carefully.

"Just a basic dark coloured one," she concludes.

"Will you be wishing a notice put in the newspaper?" I ask

"No!" she replies firmly.

"Will you be wanting to view down at the local parlour the day before the funeral?" I ask.

"Yes!" She confirms, tears welling up again. I pause for a minute to let her compose herself.

I assure Mrs Hailstones that I will pass all the arrangements straight over to the lady in her local area funeral parlour, who will co-ordinate the arrangements, and bring everything together, so that all goes smoothly on

25

the day of the funeral. I promise to conduct the funeral for her, so as it's more personal, as she has already met me. I shake her hand, and politely leave, heading out into the sudden January chill of Otago Street.

Back out in the car, I pause briefly, and breath slowly, having completed my first ever funeral arrangement. Driving back to the main office on Paisley Road, I am still entranced by the situation I have just encountered. It is tragic, but also beautiful and meaningful, a small, but intense drama of love and loss, played out in a little corner of a routine world.

Back in the office, I ask my shift boss John, to check over my first arrangement.

"Idiot!" He tuts, shaking his head. "You forgot to sell the embalming."

They have been expecting me in the Smiddy for the last few days, and when I happened to pass James the barman out on Dumbarton Road one breezy afternoon, he cheerily invites me to pop in soon for a pint of Younger No:3. . . . on the house.

I do not want to appear rude, after all, the Smiddy has been my local for a few years now, and since starting my new career, I have been simply too busy to afford the time for my regular visits. On my first day off, I make sure to pop in for a pint and a catch-up with the regulars. As soon as I enter through the Smiddy door, the corner where the regulars sit erupts with whistles and cat-calls.

"Where's your top hat?" yells one of the bottling plant ladies.

"Where's your hearse?" hollers Bill the lorry driver, "If it's parked outside and can I get a lift home?"

"Do you do estimates?" queries Jeanie the distillery tour guide.

I smile sweetly.

"Do you touch the bodies," asks Jessie, the slim, twinkling lady who works at a local flower shop.

"Yes," I reply, "With disposable gloves."

Everyone around her table listens attentively as curiosity grows along with their mild intoxication.

"And, do any of the bodies talk to you?" asks Jessie again, becoming more inquisitive.

"Yes!" I respond, seriously, "Sometimes they do."

There is a stunned silence in the bar now, and EVERYBODY is transfixed waiting for more details.

"They say," I pause, for dramatic effect,

"The things I do to escape the rubbish banter at the Smiddy!"

After a brief pause, of just a few seconds, the bar erupts in sustained laughter, and James the barman sighs in relief as a potentially bizarre situation in his hostelry resolves itself, and the atmosphere returns to normal. I buy, and drink a pint of the No:3, and it's delicious.

"So," quips James, " . . . not seen you for about three weeks ralfy!"

"How are you getting on with the new job?"

"Actually James, I'm really enjoying it, if you know what I mean, it's a 'real' job, out and about, dealing with real people in all sorts of situations, and every day is another drama."

I think for a minute about telling him about Mrs Hailstones, but I check myself, maintaining a discretion and seemliness, appropriate to my function. I take the conversation on a different direction, "So! You should see these Daimler hearses, and limousines, very classy, real walnut veneer, and button starters," I add, "Along with four litre v8 engines, which . . . " I pause, lowering my voice so that only James can hear, "Only eleven miles per gallon of fuel."

James's jaw drops, "What!" He exclaims, "That's horrendous, I get 40 from my Ford."

I just sigh a little, nodding sagely, as wee Jessie shuffles across to the bar to hear whatever we are talking about. As its funeral related, it must, of course, be interesting and useful for forthcoming gossip. I can't resist it.

"Jessie!" I say, speaking professionally, lowering my voice to a solemn tone, "I would recommend a pink-lined, dark veneer, raised lid coffin called a 'tiree' which at your size, let's say five foot five inches long, and nineteen inches across the shoulders, would be perfect for your requirements". Jessie stares at me, speechless, "Oh my god!" she blurts out, "I was thinking of exactly that when I discussed it last year with my daughters". She stares at me, "That's just spooky how you just knew that". "Oh my God . . . James, make that a double vodka and coke!" adding "How did he even know my size without a measuring tape?"

James grins, pressing a tumbler twice against an optic up on the gantry, "Don't you worry Jessie . . . its no your turn for a while yet, you will probably outlive us all what with your activities and cooshy life down at the flower shop."

"It's no' that cooshy ya bastard," retorts Jessie, "I work hard!"

"But you don't have to serve folks like Sanny the grumpy wee Cooper, do you," responds James, "givin' his opinions and cheek, and tantrums now and again".

"Aye . . . and again!" replies Jessie, "he's way too forward what with his dribbling and leering and such".

James nods sympathetically, affirming Jessie's discomfort. "Aye!" he nods, "I may have to ban him again for a few weeks, it's been a wee while since the last time."

"Are you wanting a wee single malt to go with the rest of that pint ralfy?" asks James, looking for a last minute sale. "No thanks," I reply, "I have a few malts in the house, looking for both my attention, and for my opinion, so I will skip the Bunna' till next time, but thanks for asking anyway."

I head off out into the winter chill, having solemnly blessed the still curious bar-dwellers with a few words of funereal precision. They love it. They know a real life undertaker now, and it's both creepy and entertaining at the same time.

As I make my way up the landing in the close, I hear a front door open slightly on the second floor, and Margaret pokes her head out, smiling and nodding some familiarity towards her upstairs neighbour. I stop and smile, "Thanks for the advice Margaret, so far so good, and it's great to be earning again".

"I'm so pleased for you," she adds, "I could see you getting stressed about not working, so good to know things have worked out". Margaret pauses, wanting to ask something . . . but afraid to say it. She sums up the courage and blurts it out. "You won't be bringing hearses back home will you, parking them out on the street with bodies in them?"

"No!" I reassure her, laughing, but not too much, "Company vehicles remain at Company premises, always," and I add, "So I won't be doing any 'homers' Margaret". She seems immediately reassured, and waves me 'good night' as she shuts her door to the world outside, with all its issues.

Once inside my flat on the top floor, I have a good laugh at everyone's perceptions, delusions and presumptions about my job and about funerals in general, however, in fairness, I remain mindful of the folks in the community around me, and observe a tactical remoteness when discussing my work on future occasions.

After dinner, I uncork a bottle of Glenfarclas 15yo single malt, and pour a large one into a wine glass. With a little water added, and given time, it is warming, soothing, intense, malty, sherried and very satisfying. I love it, and I drink it. So I pour another, but only one other, as I have a funeral to conduct the following day, and need to be in good condition to look after the family, and to do my duties.

The day is crisp, bright, cold, clear and calm, dappled with winter sunlight and freshness in the soft breeze which meanders slowly across the city from out of the west. Little Ted the hearse driver and myself load hearse number two at the Paisley Road premises with the coffined remains of John Hailstones, and proceed at a modest pace over the Clyde River and up Maryhill Road. On arriving at the sizeable parlour on the corner of Springbank Street, we discreetly remove the coffin from the hearse onto a folding heavy-duty stainless steel trolley and wheel the coffin in through the creaky aluminium front door towards a vacant viewing room, simple and bare, except for a small photo of old Maryhill on the wall, and a vase of plastic purple flowers on a small circular table hidden in the corner.

Little Ted is good company, one of the good guys, helpful and professional, and we get on well from the very start, so I'm glad he is helping me with this funeral in particular, as it's really the first ever funeral I have arranged. Although I have been left to get on with it, Marilyn at the Maryhill Road parlour has assured me that nothing needed changed, and nothing important was omitted from the original arrangements when I made them in Otago Street. She added the embalming after explaining it to her client.

All good then, no issues.

I check that the white lilies are fresh delivered from the florist, and look again at my daily work sheet of three funerals. The first two are completed, a direct delivery to a crematorium where the family were waiting for a short religious service. Also, a catholic funeral mass from Saint Theresas in Saracen Street, leaving the church at 10.45am after a 10am mass and proceeding to Lambhill cemetery for 11am, with the family and priest both pleasant and appreciative of my services, the hearse, car and a dry, non-wintery day, especially with it being a burial.

Suddenly Ted sticks his head round the door of the office, "That's them arriving now," he states, and as I walk outside to meet Mrs Hailstones I cross my fingers that all will go well and that there will be no mistakes or disasters along the way. As the limousine driver helps Mrs Hailstones decant from the vehicle, along with two friendly looking neighbours, I go forward to meet her, and to show her into the parlour. She clasps my hand, trembling and tearful, but resolved, and clearly with more acceptance of the situation than several day previous.

The three mourners view Mr Hailstones, paying their respects, with the two neighbours giving space to their little old friend, to kiss and mumble some partings to her beloved, her one and only. After ten minutes, I escort them back out to the limousine, and having closed the coffin, and having loaded the hearse, we proceed at about 25 miles per hour up Maryhill Road, heading north to the junction of Lochburn Road, where we turn right under the canal tunnel towards Glasgow Crematorium. It's the small chapel were going to, more intimate, and ideal for a small farewell.

As we arrive, I spot the humanist, 'cheery' John, swigging from a hip flask behind a stone pillar. "Good!" states little Ted, "'Cheery' always gives a better service after he has had a few!"

I smile to myself, briefly, cutting it off abruptly as I exit the hearse to escort the mourners inside the crematorium accompanied by the sound of organ music playing softly. Bill Smith, the manager, is on duty and proves tactful and charming in bringing over twenty years of experience to his job. After the three mourners have been seated, and checks made for anyone else attending (there are none), Bill, myself, Ted and the driver carry the coffin at waist height up seven steps and into the chapel, with large ball bearings rumbling loudly as we manoeuvre the coffin facing left to right, and sideways on the catafalque.

We pause, with Bill covering the coffin with a dark purple, velvet pall cover, then the four of us bow to the coffin, and sedately retreat from the chapel, allowing the humanist celebrant to proceed. At the end of the service, the organist strikes up a cheerful ditty, and Mrs Hailstones leads the three attendees from out of the chapel. I stand at the bottom of the steps to lead her back to the waiting limo, and once she is comfortably seated in the back, she leans forward briefly to catch my attention. "Thank you for everything Mr Mitchell, it's been so much easier than I thought it would be."

As the limousine purrs off down the narrow drive between the two little Jewish cemeteries, I give her a wave, and that is the last I ever see of Mrs Hailstones.

Strangely, although many, many years pass by, I will never forget her.

Chapter Three - The merry widows of Springburn & the silence of a lost life.

It's a funny, funny old world.

So it is.

We all make plans in life, and while were busy doing life, life goes and makes plans for us, and we hardly notice it as its happening. It is only with experience, and sufficient time to have experience, along with a good level of honest observation, that we notice how some small situation, or fleeting decision, can turn our plans and ambitions on their heads and suddenly make new ones appear, some which improve our lives, and some which don't.

I'm six months into the job now, my unexpected, accidental new career, and I am not regretting a thing. Sure, the hours are long, and the work can be stressful, especially as I still have a lot to learn. But, with *this* job, the job of being an undertaker, it is interesting, varied and meaningful. It's a job that matters, unlike so many others, which just don't, and never will. Because of this I am happy to tough it out and see how it morphs over the next few years. I might change my mind about it later, but for the moment, I am, well . . . I'm not sure I should be saying this . . . but I like my job.

I work with many good, caring people, and a few who don't care. The management are petty and indifferent, judging their success through passing distain and subdued threats, waiting for the next 'mistake' to pounce upon so that 'heads will roll', but considering the sheer volume of work, the managers often remain waiting, just waiting for the next fuck-up by one of the minions. Some members of staff are always being scrutinised, whilst others seem to get away with a lot, but that's real-life and I just get on with it.

The most serious fuck-ups are usually made by the managers, but they are never held accountable. They have status.

I have a day off today, a Friday, due as a lieu day from working a bank holiday, so I relax in the morning with a walk up Byres Road, and down

Great Western Road to the Kelvingrove Park, and into the Art Gallery. It is free to enter, and has many good exhibits. I grab a seat at the cafe in the main hall and enjoy a coffee and shortcake sitting opposite two conspiring, whispering ladies. One of them is podgy and dressed in a long black coat with a bright, arty scarf, and the other looks like a relic from the 60's with her beehive hairdo, and trashy, bright clothing, designed for someone much younger than herself. They look like they're plotting something, but it's too noisy and busy in the place to hear any of their conversation.

I finish up my drink and head on down Dumbarton Road for a quick pint at the Smiddy, catching it during the day, whilst it's quiet and more atmospheric.

When I arrive, Sanny the retired Cooper is nestling on a stool at the bar, trying to sell James the barman another bottle of unlabelled whisky. James is not in the mood, and is glad of my presence, interrupting the monologue from Sanny.

"What will it be then . . . No3?"

"Please," I reply, "And a wee half of Bunna for chasers too."

"Comin' right up," quips James, cheerily.

Sanny stares intensively down the length of the bar, eyeing me inquisitively. His grubby green fleece zipped up tight over his belly, and his puffy red nose holding a dilapidated pair of thick rimmed tortoiseshell glasses in front of his bleary eyes. He wears a ponytail, tied with an elastic, but not looking neat or tidy, it never does.

"So!" he states authoritatively, "You got a job with the co-op as an undertaker then?"

"Yes," I respond, politely.

"I could 'uv got you a job in the warehouse son . . . and then people would not be getting creeped-out by you."

"Do you touch-up the bodies?" he asks.

"How do you mean?" I respond, warily.

33

"Like, you know, touch the titties an' such!"

"Now, that's enough of that!" growls James.

"Am' just kidding," replies Sanny, looking slightly shame-faced.

"No Sanny, absolutely never . . . do I touch the 'titties', or show any disrespect at any time for anyone, and by the sounds of it, it's not the job for you! . . . so better you are a cooper."

James gives me a wink.

"Well that's your gas on a peep Sanny!" he retorts to his customer.

"A wuz only kiddin son," mumbles Sanny, than quickly changes the subject onto whisky, knowing that this is safer ground for conversation.

"Do you want to buy some more samples?" he enquires,

"No thanks Sanny," I reply briskly,

"I'm buying a few bottles along at Oddbins in Crow Road now."

"Whaaat!" he splutters, "They charge a fortune for stuff that only took pennies to make."

"I can get you samples cheap son!" he insists.

"Nope Sanny, it's time to invest in bottles, I think they will be appreciated in the future, and I will have a stash ready for when they get too expensive to buy."

"I will call it my Undertakers Stash" I exclaim with a flourish.

"It will be bottles of pure dead brilliant malt-moments."

James and Sanny both burst out laughing, lightening the mood wonderfully.

———————————————————

I am conducting a funeral today, three in fact, two in the morning and one in the afternoon, after which, hopefully, I will have time to eat some lunch. I am now getting much better at this, rapidly gaining more experience, and experience is everything in this game. If I'm not on a van, I'm on a hearse, and no two days are ever the same.

For whatever reason, it's hearse number one again today, driven by the quiet, thoughtful and serious-minded Hughie Burke, known either as

'Uncle Fester' or 'Scabbie' depending on who you talk to. I like him immediately as he is caring, helpful and sincere, unlike at least one other hearse driver who loves to shirk his duties under cover of 'shop steward' duties, and who also happens to be an arsehole.

Hughie seems to appreciate that I know I am learning, and need to pay attention to detail, and as such. I listen to his advice on funeral matters, and acknowledge his experience, which is considerable as he has been doing the job for over 20 years.

We head off out from the garage in Scotland Street, with the large Daimler engine rumbling contentedly as we head round into West Street to catch the slip road up and over the Kingston Bridge, heading north to Springburn. The coffin, flowers and anything else to do with the arrangements are all located at the Parlour in Cowlairs Road. After fifteen minutes on the road, we arrive to see John, the receptionist, outside with a mop and bucket, cleaning up yet another deposit of dogs' dirt, left by passing dog walkers, who don't care, and never will care. "Wee bastards", mumbles John to no-one in particular, leaving the mop leaning against the front door as he goes across the road to pour out the bucket of soapy water and dogs piss down a drain.

John is an odd one, a natural gentleman, soft in nature, too soft in fact, and he regularly gets teased as being the 'branch lady' at Cowlairs. He looks like a member of the Home Guard, straight out of 'Dads Army', a classic BBC series. "The family are lovely," he informs us as I pass through the large service chapel to check the viewing room at the back of the parlour, checking for flowers, checking the body, I.D. condition, appearance, checking everything and anything to ensure that all is as it should be. Hughie disappears back out to the hearse for a smoke.

"Bit odd, this one," declares John, ruffling through the pile of arrangements on his office desk, pulling put the details of the funeral I'm about to conduct. "The deceased has no family as such, just a group of friends, who all stay up the same block of flats in Balgrayhill". He pauses, examining again the arrangements he's made, "Seems they are all living in the same block, and are all widows, and are now a sort of family

35

themselves. They call themselves the merry widows. They're well known in the community, supporting some local charities, and organising bus trips for the locals who need a wee trip down to Largs and such places!"

I smile, grinning at the thought of the local pensioner posse, keeping it real, etc.

He continues, "Seems they play the stock market as a club, and do quite well out of it".

I listen now, a little more closely to John. " . . . and get a lot of wins at the Bingo too, which pays for the buses and days-out". Hughie pokes his head around the door, "That's the car arriving now."

I head out to meet the ladies, and even as the limousine glides towards the front door, I hear laughter and banter from out of the opened back windows. Bill Smith, the wiry, alert, and humorous driver flashes me a grin from behind the wheel, bringing the mourners to a gentle halt immediately outside the parlour door. Bill leaps out to open the doors for the funeral attendees, although it looks more like a girls-club day out at the fun fair!

I approach the bossiest looking lady, who appears to be organising all the others, and introduce myself; "Hello Mrs Shire, I'm ralf, and I'm looking after things for the family today". "Oh goody!" replies Mrs Shire, a tall, peroxide blond, well dressed, and remarkably cheery for such an occasion.

"Lead on then ralf," she quips, and I gesture the ladies to enter the parlour and to take a seat in the service room, where the five of them sit in a huddle and resume their conversation, interrupted at the point that the limo decanted them at the door.

I wander through to the office, where John is sitting, hunched by a wall heater, and sipping from a mug of cold tea. "No viewing then?" I ask. "No," replies John, "They're just sitting for ten minutes and then want to see us load the coffin onto the hearse, and then to follow on in the car, up to Glasgow crematorium for a wee service from the minister". I pause, puzzled at the sound of prolonged laughter emanating from the service room. "They seem very cheery for bereaved friends!" I suggest. "Been like that from the moment they all came in to make arrangements seven days ago." replies John, finishing off what's left of his drink. "They seem very at ease with the situation, sort of, *concerned*, but not particularly bothered". I pause to reflect for a few seconds, "Oh! Well," I add, "different strokes for different folks I suppose".

John just nods . . . then goes off to put the kettle on again.

Soon, I am leading the mourners out to the limousine, where Bill the driver, stands, hat on, and to attention, with limmousine doors ready-opened, assisting the ladies into the vehicle, and ensuring their seatbelts are fastened. Bill, Hughie and myself, trolley the sealed coffin, with the flower on top of the lid, out of the parlour, and into the hearse, rolling it over the bier rollers smoothly into the security of six, well placed retaining pins.

As a cortege, we glide down the road and up to Hawthorn Street, which leads directly to Glasgow crematorium with the least involvement of traffic lights. As the funeral party passes slowly along Tresta Road, we arrive at the imposing Victorian gates of the Western necropolis cemetery, where, with a sharp right turn, a slight inclined drive leads us round to the front door of the old chapel of Glasgow crematorium, one of the oldest crematoriums in the British Isles, opening for services in 1895, and never stopping since then. At the top of an imposing flight of gothic stairs stand two sombre gothic-looking men.

One is Tam the crematorium attendant, tall, organised and consistent. The other is the Reverend Hutchison, affectionately known in undertakers circles as 'Wheech McGhee' due to his succinct, direct, and rapid committal services. He looks imposing, dressed in his long his black gown and white crossed preaching bands, flapping around his neck.

As soon as the cortege stops, I alight and climb the steps to greet the minister and Tam, both of whom indicate clearly not to waste any time, and to hustle the mourners into the chapel. Once briefly settled, Tam joins us to carry in the coffin onto the raised marble catafalque, where after, I assist in draping a plush purple velvet pall cloth over the coffin and we all retire. The service commences, quickly, but tastefully.

"My god, wait till you here this," gasps Bill, as we get into the limo for a chat, whilst the service is happening. "That lot in the back are something else!"

Hughie and I wait for more. "They are all part of some kind of club, a widows' club, so when a husband dies, the widow joins the club and they pool their pensions then look after one another, where their own families are no longer interested. After several of them had wins a few years back in the bingo, they started to invest in the stock market, and they seem to be very good at backing winners, so much so that they have bought a big holiday villa in Tenerife now where they go together every winter for at least three months".

He pauses, looking for our response, "Can you believe it?" he concludes.

My expression and Hughie's too, affirm that we are both mightily surprised at the situation. It seems that the ladies have been quite revealing on the road up to the crematorium.

The service is probably about to end soon, so Bill makes it quick with one more disclosure; "And the deceased has bypassed her family and left all her money to the community to pay for education grants for local kids who want to go to college or uni', so quite a woman then, the deceased!"

We hear the clunk of the doors opening again up the steps, and Tam emerges, grey and sombre, leading the mourners back down the stairs to their awaiting vehicle. At the same time Hughie quietly moves the hearse down the drive a few metres, taking it out of immediate sight of the funeral party as they breeze off down the drive and back to Springburn for a reception at the Hawthorn Bar.

We head back down the road to the parlour in Cowlairs to collect some paperwork for the office. We arrive to find John deep in conversation with a cheery old man at the front door. The old fella is clearly intoxicated and eager to tell John that family will probably want to see the body of a young drugs victim who has been pulled from the canal just up the road, and was in the water for about a week, so fish have been feeding. John nods reassuringly, then waves the drunk on his way, grateful for the timely arrival of the justifiable distraction in the form of a hearse.

Once inside the office with the outside door closed securely to ensure a bit more privacy, John tuts with exasperation and switches on the kettle.

"That's Jeremy the local drunk, always nosy about funeral business and wanting to know who's dead in case he knows them".

Then he adds "He's never through sticking his head through the door and I even caught him looking at an arrangement recently," shaking his head and clearly exasperated with the intruder.

"Then!" he continues, "He said that the cost of the flowers was what he gets every month as added state benefit specifically for alcohol addiction, bearing in mind that he's not worked for over twenty years now, and gets all the benefits going".

"So how much then?" I ask.

"180 pounds extra!" replies John, " . . . and that's every month!" he concludes abruptly.

Hughie decides it's time to move the conversation on, just as the kettle comes to the boil, and so changes the subject. The chat turns to the group of ladies we have just completed a funeral for, up at the crematorium.

"Well then," says John, drawing closer across his desk, and pushing two hot mugs of watery tea towards us. "So, two of them came in to make arrangements, but I knew one from the bingo, and she had a big win a few years back, and that's about when the Girls Club started, and they became famous locally for all the charity stuff they do with fund-raising and such". John pauses to stir his tea a little colder.

"They have now paid for quite a few local kids to go to college, and even some to go to university. It's a group of six widows, all local girls, who stay on the same three landings up in the Balgreyhill flats. They're really smart and play the stock market and make so much money, they bought a villa somewhere around Spain, where they over-winter every year for two or three months".

"They are local celebrities." he concludes.

"I suppose they just made opportunities for themselves, and got lucky, and have never looked back. . . . And, here's me stuck in the funeral parlour, having to make a basic living, with no stocks and shares and no free hand-outs, and no free money for alcohol!" moans John.

"But time to sit around all day in a cosy office, slurping tea and eating digestive biscuits," notes Hughie.

John shrugs!

"I think much of life is what we choose to make it John," I offer as way of explanation.

"I suppose so," sighs the parlour receptionist, cosy in his office, left alone to his own devices, interrupted now and again by families needing to make arrangements, making the most with what they have.

Back at the main office, Hughie drops me off and heads back up the road to the Scotland Street garage, whilst I look for a corner in the kitchen to have a sandwich I brought to work with me in the morning but have yet not had a chance to eat. John Farrell slides his ample belly in past the door frame and demands to know why I'm not in the office processing arrangements. "Listen son, I'm getting pinned to the wall, and blown out the sky with all the arrangements coming over, so we need all hands on deck," he splutters.

Suddenly big Alec the van driver appears, "Listen John," he states, "If I don't get someone on the van now we are never going to get todays work in from the hospitals. Andy Barr has disappeared, apparently taking a form out to a family, and I need another man". John turns to me, panicking again, as he does regularly in such occasions, "Just you go with Alec ralf . . . and hurry back as soon as you can".

Out in the van as we glide off along to the southern general hospital, Alec, who's driving again, bursts out laughing then lights another cigarette. "So I saved you from being stuck in the office . . . again," he grins. "Yes, thanks Alec, I appreciate being rescued from the chaos." I respond, grateful for the sudden change, and munching discreetly on my sandwich.

At the hospital we load a body on a stretcher into the van, and along with the b&c cremation papers receive a short written message, handed over by Willie, the abrupt and mischievous mortician. The note reads -

URGENT

police removal in the gorbals, 50 Braehead St to City Mortuary, and needs done v-quickly as is a cot-death.

J.F.

Alec sighs, "Well here we go, so much for getting our hospital work done today".

We quickly head off back down Paisley Road via the Paisley Road office to pick up what is called the 'pipers box' - a plain wooden case, 36 inches in length and for the purpose of transporting infants. Then we drive into the gorbals, and along Caledonia Road towards the address . . . it does not take long to arrive at a modern council, three-floor flat, nestled out of the way, and adjacent to an old part of the southern necropolis cemetery. Alec spies the police van first and manoeuvres as close as he can to ensure minimal walking distance to the house. We disembark and head to the ground floor flat, visible due to the sound of inconsolable wailing from a mother within.

As soon as we have gently knocked the door, a pale and shaken policewoman appears, ushering us to stay put till she can separate the mother and father from their child. It takes a few minutes, but eventually, a broken woman is helped by her partner into the kitchen and the door is half closed to allow some final remaining contact between mother and child not to be broken. I gesture to Alec as to whether I should quickly go to the van and remove the pipers box, but he silently gestures an affirmative no.

A now tearful policewoman appears again from behind the front door gesturing us in and urging us to be a quick as possible as the mother is now screaming for her baby, struggling against the father who himself is sobbing loudly, holding her back as best he can. The situation suddenly impacts me, and my own emotion is touched intensely by the pain of others, washing like a wave of hurt across my heart. Alec places a hand on my shoulder. "Just stay here," he says softly.

He walks into the house, into the front room, lifts the dead baby from its cot, and swiftly reappears again, acknowledging the policewoman, and urges me to join him in returning speedily to the van where we head off quietly back down Caledinia Road towards the city mortuary.

"Where's the baby?" I ask, still slightly shocked and distracted with my emotions.

He unzips his anorak, nestled inside against his shirt is the swaddled shape of a tiny lifeless infant.

"The pipers box would have been too much for the situation," he explains, "The best thing under the circumstances was to get in and out as soon, and as discreetly as possible".

Alec sighs deeply, "You see ralfy, you will get used to much of this job, but when it's a baby, it brings some pain to everyone, so thank goodness for small mercies that they are so few and far between in this country."

The baby remains within Alec's jacket all the way, and then into the mortuary, where a soft silence is respected by staff for the situation, an undeniable and indelible situation, for the pain of a mother losing her baby is the greatest pain of all, the deepest hurt, . . . the most unforgetable.

At home, later in the day, having finished work, a long shift, busy and eventful, I eat beans on toast for dinner and then light the fire in the grate, adding a lot more coal than usual. Soon, the flames roar, and the heat builds wonderfully, then I pour a glass of Laphroaig, then another, then another. The liquor sooths the tempest of the day, with its drams and events, and I slowly lose sobriety in a comforting way.

Despite the warmth, I shiver suddenly, thinking of the drama within my day, which seems so much longer ago, more than just a few hours. Here in my flat in Gardner Street, I am safe, detached and secured from the reality of other people's experiences. I pour another glass of Laphroaig, the

10 year old cask strength version, and then I add a little water to chase out the flavours. There's no point in pouring any other single malt now, as I will never taste it anyway, not after the Laphroaig.

I fall asleep suddenly by the fireside, and dream of nothing.

Two days later, John waddles along the corridor, arrangement in hand, and breezes purposefully into the office, wafting the details in the air like a court summons.

"Ralf, . . . mate, tha's an arrangement for you, and I've told the family you will be with them in 30 minutes".

He thrusts the arrangement request details at me and quickly turns to walk back to his comfy office where he can close the door and read a newspaper.

"Excuse me John," I interject, "But this is a baby arrangement, and I haven't been shown how to go about them yet".

"Nothing to it!" he splutters. "Just get the basics and the family can do the rest at the parlour, anyway, they will be too upset to say much. He pauses briefly before concluding,

". . . and don't hang about, you can get it all done in 10 minutes. I need you back for the office a soon as."

I walk up the road from the Paisley Road office to the garage in Scotland Street, and ask Mannie Secluna, the garage manager, for the keys to a standard black estate car. He glances briefly at my arrangement, pausing to scan the details. He is a small, bespectacled, grey haired, fidgety man, originally from Malta, and affectionately known in Scotland Street by his staff as the 'maltese budgie'.

"What are they giving you that for?" he demands. "Are you not a bit inexperienced to be getting baby arrangements so soon?

Your only eight months in the job,

is there no one more experienced to do it?"

"No!" I reply, "I will just get on with it, and see how it goes". Mannie hands over a set of car keys, shaking his head and tutting to himself. "Bloody shambles of a place . . . well good luck son, and let me know how you get on".

In the car I look again at the arrangements information, this time in more detail;

a name,

a contact phone number,

a mother, father and grandmother,

and an address,

. . . 50 Braehead Street, Gorbals.

I take a very deep breath, start the car, and head out and along Caledonia Road back to the flat. As I arrive at my destination, and after switching off the ignition, slowly, reluctantly getting out of the car, I feel already that I am leaving a safety zone, and confronting a situation for which I am not prepared. I knock the door, softly, gently, so as not to break the gravity of the situation. Soon a young man answers, the father, civil, ordinary, unassuming, and he silently gestures me into the home, indicating me towards the kitchen at the back.

I walk in carefully, not taking a seat until directed by an older woman, the grandmother.

Everyone has been crying, and it shows. Tissues lay strewn on the table and some early-delivered bereavement cards sit opened, read and then discarded.

The mother looks very young, no more than nineteen, and her partner is not much older than her. He sits down next to her then holds her.

She is silent, she is numb, and it seems to me suddenly, again, that a mother's loss of a baby child is the deepest loss a human can endure.

This sudden awareness never leaves me for the rest of my life.

In silence I open my arrangement case and remove the plain black folder which contains everything I need to make arrangements. The older woman immediately takes to answering my questions.

"Will it be a cremation or a burial?

Will you be wanting some flowers arranged for you ?

Will you be leaving from the house or the local parlour to go to the cemetery?

Would you like a limousine provided for the family?"

Arrangements don't take long, although the silence and numb-calm within the house makes time pass very slowly. The grandmother holds it together well, and we get a lot of detail recorded on my arrangement sheet. The father sits, head in hands, now separate from his partner, lost in his own thoughts. The mother says nothing. The grandmother seems relieved at her own strength to make the arrangements.

I am soon concluded, advising that any further details can be communicated with a visit or phone call to the local parlour in Aitkenhead Road. I don't shake hands, or offer sincerest condolences, and I don't try to be breezy and efficient. I keep it real as the situation is very real to the family.

I leave, seeing myself out of the front door, and after shutting it firmly, I pause on the front step, allowing the mist of pain and loss within the flat, to blow gently away on the cool, winter wind, blowing gently and indifferently across the street.

I breathe suddenly, deeply, of the cold fresh air.

An old woman, hunched and life-weathered, shuffles by looking to engage me with eye contact, "Just so sad and tragic, and such a loss!" she exclaims, moving on by without waiting to register my response. I walk to the car, get in, turn on the ignition and drive down the road a few hundred yards before pulling into the kerb and switching off the engine. I lower the windows on both sides and breathe deeply from the cold air blowing across from the cemetery next door. I feel like some of the house I've just been in is still with me now, haunting me with its presence. I sit still and look over the railings of the cemetery a few yards away, beholding an angel, wings spread wide, grey and as cold as the granite from which it has been carved. I wonder if an angel will be there for the family, for the mother, for the baby.

45

A small bird, a robin, lands on the head of the angel, singing lustily and hopping around. I find myself returning again to the ordinary-ness of the day, just another day, and typically anonymous of the world in which we live. I start the engine again with a twist of the ignition key and head on down Caledonia Road, back to Paisley Road, and to the office.

That night I light the fire in my hearth, then after some thought, light a candle in the back window of my flat, watching the yellow flame flicker and glow for a while.

It seems the right thing to do in the remains of the day.

It helps me return to some sort of normal.

But not the normal of yesterday.

Chapter Four – Mr Brown & a terrible accident with a hearse.

I'm standing outside a shop in Byres Road, in the west-end of Glasgow, looking in through a large picture window at shelves and shelves of whiskies all lined up like soldiers on parade. I peruse them quickly, then scrutinise them for a few minutes in more detail as the day is unusually bright and sunny with a mild air blowing down the road from the botanic gardens, so it's nice to be standing there on the pavement.

It is a lovely day, and now I'm in the mood, suddenly, to buy some bottles of whisky. I walk through the purple-painted front door, and catch the eye of George, the young manager of Peckham's delicatessen. He grins as he looks up from the counter, seeing me full of purchasing-business. George is slim, tidy, sometimes moody, but always professional, looking like an academic or a librarian who simply got stuck in a job he only intended as a stop-gap. I think a failed relationship had something to do with his situation, but, I would never ask about such a thing.

Poised by the till, "What's it today ralfy?" he asks. "Bottle of Highland Park 12yo George," I reply, "and one of the Lagavulin 16yo's, in fact, make that two. And one of the cask strength Caol Ila!"

George interjects, "Beautiful one that, and nobody wants it because it's not Macallan."

I continue, "Three of the Springbank 10yo". George pauses, displaying yet again his honesty and decency, "That one's only 23 pounds in Waitrose up the top of the road, so do you still want three?" he asks. "No, make it one bottle then and I will take a bottle of Macallan 18yo just right of the middle above your head, and that Independent bottling on the top shelf of Port Ellen". George reaches for a wooden ladder, poised patiently at the end of the shelves. He wraps the purchases in tissue paper, puts them all in a strong plastic bag, and takes my cash. I breeze out of Peckams feeling pleased with myself as I did not buy any of their fabulous cream cakes, although I was tempted.

Back in the flat, I put down the heavy bags, and put on the kettle. It was not too bad until I arrived at Waitrose supermarket at the top of the road, where the extra three bottles of Springbank 10yo's on sale at an amazing £23 a bottle soon had me queuing at the checkout and digging more cash from my wallet. On the way back home, although it was downhill most of the way, the weight of ten bottles became more and more stressful on my arms. The last bit, climbing up the stairs of the close, is torture with the weight of the bags.

Whilst the kettle is heating, I open my small walk-in cupboard in the front room and examine the shelves; there must be at least 285 bottles now, all sealed and upright, arranged in regional order with some space at the end for any other spirits. I will very shortly add ten more. The cupboard is my stash of fine malt whisky, all good stuff, and though I'm spending a fortune these days on liquor, it seems the right thing to be doing. I am getting compulsive about it, obsessive even, and I don't intend to stop. I call the collection my stash. . . . the undertakers stash.

The kettle clicks-off the boil and a hot mug of fresh-brewed tea is made, accompanied with a wee seat at the open kitchen window with a cigarette. The window is on the third floor and overlooks Partick Bowling Club green in Fortrose Street, and beyond is the West Of Scotland Cricket ground in Peel Street.

On a Saturday afternoon, on a sunny summer's day, you can see the old folks playing bowls and the younger ones having a round of cricket beyond. I hear the clink of bowls and the thwack of willow on leather, and feel at ease. But it's still winter, and it's getting cooler, so I finish my cigarette before the chilly wind chills the room too much. I really should give up, ciggies cost a fortune these days, £2.50 a pack. It used to be £1.80, prices are soaring these days. Also, I have been noticing a 'heavy chest' recently, and should heed the warnings.

With the second cup of tea cooling rapidly in my hand, I shuffle back through the hall to the 'Stash' cupboard, where I turn on the light inside then walk into the cramped space, half-closing the door behind me so that I am more wrapped around by the exotic collection of bottles.

Starting in the Lowlands, I have three bottles of Auchentoshan, two of St: Magdeline, two of Glenkinchie (which I don't enjoy so much) and a bottle of Bladnoch, which is beautifully cereally, and with a lovely flavour of lemons and oranges. I make a mental note to visit the distillery one day, even though it is rather remote, tucked away in the south-west corner of the nation. Then there are the Highlanders, one of Glenturret, Glenmorangie, and Dalmore which has a lovely shaped bottle, and five bottles of Glengoyne, which is the distillery I love to visit the most due to its secluded location and intimate size. I love the 12yo version, and plan to buy older aged bottlings, although I am put off by the cost. Glengoyne is an expensive malt.

The Speyside stash has the most number of bottles, really, about one hundred bottles of everything Speyside'ish. Islay is well represented with ten bottles each of Laphroaig, Bowmore, Ardbeg, Caol Ila, and Lagavulin, whilst in the Island sector, there are only two bottles, a Highland Park, and a Talisker. I opened the Talisker recently, but unexpectedly, did not enjoy it so much on first acquaintance. I'm not sure why!

Finally, there is the Campbeltown section, represented by eight bottles of Springbank.

I notice what's left of my tea is cold. I switch off the cupboard light and seeing as I have a second day off in a row, which is unusual these days, I prepare some beans on toast with a couple of poached eggs on top for dinner, then head out and down to the Smiddy, for a pint of No:3.

Sanny's been barred again, no surprise there, and Jessie is not feeling well, so no change there then either. She blames her ill-health on all the customers coming into the off-sales where she works, and passing on their germs which means she can't go to the spiritualist church meetings with her friends.

James frowns to himself as he hands over a glass of fresh-poured No:3 and looks into the middle distance from behind the bar, suddenly deep in thought, as if putting together pieces of a puzzle.

"You know," he states, "that Sanny is just not himself at the moment, and he must have something weighing heavy on his mind, what with all his

49

behaviour recently, and now having to be barred." Jessie is sitting in the corner with Alice, the two of them mulling over dubonet and gins, when she suddenly pipes up, as if reading Jame's thoughts. "Sanny was like the way he is now when he lost his pal Robert a few years back, do you remember?" she reminds James. "Aye, right enough Jessie," he affirms, "Robert and he worked together for forty years, and were like brothers, what with Robert keeping Sanny grounded and away from that nagging wife of his". "She's a trouble-maker," mutters Jessie from behind her glass, having just taken a sip, " And she's only tolerates him for his money, and for staying out of her way while she's spending it".

Alice sitting beside her nods, agreeing silently.

I watch over the conversation in front of me feeling mildly uneasy, sensing something I'm missing, and something not being said by the others around me, something I'm not allowed to know.

"You're off the hearse now and on the van and your leaving soon . . . because that's a directive," splutters John Farrell, who has just waddled out of the manager's office and up to the desk where the hearse work for the day is neatly arranged in a row. Hughie the hearse driver looks on silently, almost apologetically, and as John huffs his way back out he shuffles forwards to clarify the sudden change of plan. "I know we're scheduled with me for these three today son, but the family on the last funeral have requested Andy Barr to conduct, as, supposedly, they know him", he pauses, thinking, then concludes, "but I'm not so sure, I think he's just swingin' it for an easy day."

Andy Barr walks into the room, having just finished another cigarette at the front door, and grins. "A' know the family on the last one, so you're now on the van with big Alec." he pauses for some drama, "And that's a bastard of a heavy one you're getting our the Western Infirmary," he laughs and lifts his hearse work for the day, an easy day by the look of it.

Hughie has seen this stunt before, I can tell by the actively passive expression across his weathered face. My esteemed colleague, and funeral director, Andy Barr is an ugly man in the fullest sense, being sleekit, cunning, and with a wasted intelligence which could have allowed him to achieve a lot more in life . . . but that was never his ambition. Making his work as easy as possible, smoking, and arranging as large an overtime claim as he possibly can . . . these are his ambitions, followed by routine nights in bars, alone, and drinking cheap beers as sour and stale as his humanity. His pinched face, dark demeanour and lack of sympathy for others seem to define his role in life.

I don't like him.

He knows it.

Thus, he acknowledges the situation by stealing my good days of hearse work and replacing them with his heavy days of van work. John Farrell, who is a 'friend' of Andy, ensures Andy gets his way . . . always. They are old 'pals', and Andy has 'stuff' on John too, so John is best to play along.

I give Hughie a knowing wink, "Have a good day old-timer," I grin. Hughie just rolls his eyes, "At least I can guarantee an easy day now with no house removals," he mutters.

I wander off, round the back to the loading bay on Laidlaw Street to meet Alec and the van. As we head off down the road Alec turns to be grinning like a Cheshire cat, "So is that you getting fucked-over again by Andy Barr?"

"Yes." I reply, flatly.

Alec laughs out loud. "Well," he adds, thoughtfully, "Someone else is being left alone today then cos' it's your turn for a shafting. And by the way," he adds, "We've got a big one from out of the Western Infirmary this morning."

At the first destination of our day's work, Allan, mortuary technician at the Royal Infirmary hands us a note as soon as we arrive - a message from the office. As there are no hearses available, Alec and I are to take the van to the east end, to 'The Sanctuary' in Buckingham Drive, Carmyle, and uplift a deceased from their home, and it's urgent, lawyers have been in touch, and lawyers are a priority with the Co-op Funeral Service.

We speed from the Royal Infirmary along the London Road, and off towards the river Clyde and Carmyle, a small compact village, locked between the river and a motorway leaving it separated and somehow removed and remote from the greater city sprawl of Glasgow. It is an oddly, detached place, and Buckingham Drive is an oddly, detached cul-de-sac separated from Carmyle. It is almost a world of its own.

We arrive at the front gate of a neat brown sandstone bungalow, nestled between mature trees, and all is quiet, with birds trilling and cheeping within the boughs of the opulent greenery. A soft and gentle breeze blows cool air around us as we exit the van, acknowledging a small, frail lady standing at the front door who is catching our attention by waving a brown chequered tea towel.

At her feet sits a large and unusually brown-coloured cat with ebony eyes, staring at us with mild disinterest. Alec and I alight from the van, and as I remove a folded aluminium stretcher from out of the back, Alec greets the woman at the front door. The situation is simple, a youngish man, of which little information provided, has passed away peacefully in his sleep, and the police will not be involved. His doctor has been swiftly in attendance to issue the death certificate, and the body is now clear to be removed.

I walk up the seven steps to the front door which is a lustrous gloss mahogany brown, and am ushered into the house by the little lady, who seems uncomfortable. Inside, both Alec and I stop and stare in a moments silence at what is in front of us. Everything, without exception is a shade of brown; wallpaper, furniture, carpets, fixtures and fittings, all brown. The whole place looks like a sepia image devoid of any colour apart from a hundred shades of brown.

We are ushered into the main front room where the death certificate and a partly completed cremation form lay sitting on a table. It is now that we feel the presence of the building envelop us. It is very, very strange, almost as if we have been transported to another dimension and

52

completely removed from the world around us. Hanging above a small brown-tiled Edwardian fireplace hangs a large portrait oil painting. A figure of a man, well, a sort-of human gazes from within the centre of the painting, almost reaching out into the room itself, expressionless and riveting.

Alec seems mesmerised by its presence.

I find it oddly unsettling and I sense a strange energy coming from the portrait.

The figure is very well dressed, almost formal wear, with a bow tie and a large bejewelled cane, looking longer than it needs to be. The environment in which he stands appears surreal, almost alien, somewhere familiar but unworldly. "He painted that one picture over the last fifteen years, working on it every day for hours," interjects the little lady, breaking the spell on the two of us.

"Very talented painter," says Alec. "Yes," replies the little lady, "He was a very talented person". We can tell she does not want to talk much. "I will show you to where he is, but mind your feet on the carpet, it's a bit loose at the back of the house. We are led through to the back of the bungalow, along a brown decorated corridor, and into a large bedroom containing a squat four-poster bed, resplendent in brown and cream pillows, covers and sheets.

A small, red-haired man lays motionless, eyes shut and mouth half-closed, as if already prepared for his coffin. Alec and I lift him carefully onto the now unfolded stretcher on which we have placed a sheet of white plastic, which now looks absurdly bright in the sepia room. I look up briefly to make a comment to Alec, but he gestures silence, and we complete our task quietly adjusting the brown pyjamas and dressing gown which he is wearing, then folding over the plastic sheet, securing the deceased with two adjustable canvas buckle straps before placing a red canvas cover over the top of the sheet, the elasticated sides of the cover, curling neatly round the frame so as to keep things tidy.

We carry him out to the van, which Alec has described to the little lady as a 'private ambulance' and having checked the provided forms, slowly

53

head off back onto the main road, returning to the Co-op mortuary in Paisley Road.

"Is it just me?" asks Alec, "or was that house a weird place."

"It's not just you." I reply. "that was very weird."

Later that day, Andy Barr swans into the office just as I am completing my paperwork, Hughie following him to make sure that a proper explanation is given for the fact that they have been missing for several hours since their last funeral. None of the managers ask, and nobody seems to care where they have been. "How did your last funeral go Andy?" I enquire politely. "Lovely," he breezes, patting his pocket with one hand. "And how was that big huge body out of the Western?" he grins. "Not clear till tomorrow Andy, so you will be getting it after all . . . unless you are requested again for a funeral!" He glares at me intensely, then heads out to the front door for a cigarette with his pal Boaby Gray.

Mr Dick saunters into the office, hands in pockets, stares at his staff intently for a few seconds, then turns around and walks back off to his office where he firmly closes the door behind him.

He does not seem to have much respect for his employees.

They do not seem to like him much either.

It's all part of the culture of the Co-op.

Ron Farrell shuffles towards me with a job sheet in his hand. "You've to arrange that funeral for the body you picked up today, at a lawyer's office in town, some wee woman at the house requested you, but I don't know why! And you've not to arrange till the day after tomorrow, at 11am sharp." He heads off into the kitchen to heat a couple of large pies for a snack before he goes home for his dinner. The smell of meat and pastry from the steaming microwave makes me hungry too, after all, it's been a busy day again with little time for lunch, and it will be busy tomorrow again.

The Smiddy is a noisy place as I enter in, escaping the cold rain now lashing down Dumbarton Road and leaving nothing in its path un-wetted. James is busy and has no time for chat, so I grab the pint of fresh-poured No:3 and head over towards Jessie who is sitting in the corner with a couple of her pals, Alice and Margaret, my neighbour from the landing downstairs. They welcome me into their group as if anticipating the opportunity to question me. Jessie dives in with a brief acknowledgment of welcome, as Margaret and Alice get ready with the questions. "So, ralfy, how's the job going, are you settling in yet?" asks Margaret disarmingly. "Fine, just fine, it takes a lot of time to pick things up, as there's such a lot to learn, but I'm getting there thanks to the support and consideration of the people I work with. There's a few arseholes, right enough, but generally everyone is fine, except for the management who just don't want to know!"

The ladies nod respectfully. There is a pause, slightly awkward, as the ladies stare at each other, waiting to see who goes first. Jessie goes first, and chimes in with, "And do you ever come across anything unusual or unexpected?" she enquires. "Not really," I reply, thinking about how much I should be revealing about the eccentric nature of the job. Jessie seems a little frustrated at my lack of candour, "But, do you not notice anything, well, if you know what I mean . . . *spooky!*"

Alice immediately jumps in, tutting with exasperation at Jessie, who now realises that her choice of words are overly dramatic. "No Jessie, not spooky, you'll never get the right answer putting it that way." she snaps. "What Jessie means," continues Margaret, "Is, do you notice anything *spiritual* in your daily dealings with families and the corpses?"

"Yes," I reply solemnly, "I do!"

The three ladies gasp in anticipation, placing down their drinks on the table.

"I notice that I'm drinking more whisky than I used to." I reply, honestly.

There are brief gasps, then silence around the table at my flippancy, and then as they continue to listen, I say some more, to defuse the situation, "But I do know that some families have very unusual situations and experiences when loved ones die."

"Tell us more," demands Margaret.

55

"And I have not seen it for myself yet, but I know that my more experienced colleagues have come across some curious situations with funerals, as if happenstance and happenings pre-ordained just happen."

"You will see it for yourself soon enough." abruptly states Alice. She is dressed comfortably and neatly in black, with little adornment or accessories. She wears no make-up and is clearly an intelligent woman of some authority.

Jessie can see that I'm looking a little uncomfortable, so changes the direction of the conversation. "We are all members of the spiritualist church along the road at Charing Cross," she informs me, "And we have just been at a service this afternoon and an unexpected spirit joined us . . . specifically mentioning you!"

I feel a tingle of discomfort run up my spine . . . and say nothing.

"We have been told by the presence to say to you that you are to do the best you can with the job, and treat it like a mission, to help and to support those at the gates of passing."

"Thanks." I reply, avoiding eye contact, "I will do that then". There is a sigh around the table as the three ladies conclude their primary mission, and things lighten considerably when I offer to buy them a round of drinks.

Later on that evening, as I accompany a less sober Margaret back to the flat, she confides to me that the 'presence' said more than I have been initially lead to believe. "You see," says Margaret as we climb the stairs inside the close, "The presence was not nasty or hostile ralfy, in fact, if anything, calm, caring and friendly". I immediately feel reassured on hearing this. "Sort of understanding and acknowledging that you are the right person to do what you do. And I know you think of us as daft old bats, but it's true, there is the 'other side', and we are not told the truth by society. I got a feeling you will be meeting this presence, whom-ever it is sometime, but I don't know when".

Margaret smiles, then heads through her door, leaving me to ascend the final flight of stairs to my flat where all is calm and as it should be, with no 'presences' lurking in the corner of the kitchen. I have my dinner, then pour a dram, drink it, refill the glass, drink it, then fall asleep, a deep and dreamless sleep, untroubled by madding world around me.

Two days later, I am taking the underground train from West Street into Argyle Street, as parking cars in the city centre is a nightmare. Passengers stare at me discreetly, shuffling their newspapers or magazines, to help shield them from the young man, neatly dressed in undertaker's garb. I remain passive, and deliberately remote, sensing their curiosity and mild repulsion. I can almost hear them thinking, 'creepy bastard' and I want to laugh, but I don't, I'm getting better with the dead-pan poker face these days, a lot better.

The office of Carr Booth & Co: is discreetly placed in a magnificent sandstone building located in West Campbell Street, and I am expected. Mister Carr, an immaculately dressed lawyer, invites me into his office with some animated arm gestures and directs me to a solid oak chair in front of his ample mahogany desk, then sits with his back to a large sash window, where he can see my face clearly, but I can't quite see his. He hands me a neatly typed written sheet of paper.

"These are all the details you will need." he states breezily.

"Practical, simple, nothing opulent." he adds.

I look at the paper. 'Yandryjin Ozmyrissa Cyarnos MacLoedd' it states, continuing, 'body direct to Daldowie crematorium, one week today at 9am, no flowers, no paper notice, clergy provided by family. Simple dark brown coffin, lined in brown interior and with brown handles'.

I look up at the lawyer, and am immediately met with a question,

"Can you supply a brown hearse young man," asks the arranger.

"I will certainly ask if it's possible to locate one."

"If you can't," he adds, "a grey one will do, Daimler Benz I believe?" he enquires.

"Yes," I reply, "That's what we use at the moment."

"Good." replies Mr Carr, clearly happy not to have been asked any solicitous questions.

"And will you conduct the funeral please?" he asks, leaning back in his chair and twirling a fountain pen in both hands.

"Not a problem, happy to do it." I respond reassuringly.

One week later I am in a brown hearse, borrowed from a Funeral Directors in Edinburgh. Myself and Hughie the driver, slide silently and slowly at 8.55am up the drive towards Daldowie crematorium, a classy, simple deco-style building in the south east corner of Glasgow. Mr Carr, the little lady from the house and a jolly-looking Franciscan monk, stand at the door, surveying our progress as the hearse eases to a silent stop in front of the steps, up, and into the west chapel of the building.

With the assistance of crematorium staff, we carry at waist height, the coffin containing the 'brown man' down the chapel aisle and up onto the catafalque, where the monk after a brief blessing, allows us to place a double ended spray of cream lilies with brown leaves intertwined in front of the head of the coffin. We step back, bow, turn, and depart the chapel leaving the mourners standing and awaiting the service and committal.

Out of nosiness, I linger at the doors listening as best I can to what is being said inside, however, the entire service is in a strange and seemingly ancient language, as far as I can make out, so I never know anything more about the strange and eccentric 'Mr Brown'.

At the end of the service, Mr Carr the lawyer approaches me to say thank you, and sensing my curiosity adds, "Mr MacLoedd was a very talented linguist, and thinker. He served our country in ways you could never understand."

Soon the mourners depart and Hughie and myself head off back to the garage to change the borrowed brown hearse for our more familiar grey one.

That same afternoon we are heading up Balmore Road from Saracen Street parlour with a burial at the western necropolis extension cemetery, when the first flurry of hail and snow arrives, bringing a chill and dressing of fine white ice flakes onto the road ahead of us. "Oh, here we go Hughie, you can see over the hills that this is going to get worse," I say, and within five minutes a carpet of fresh icy snow flakes lays across the road and surrounding houses like a dusting of icing over a sponge cake.

As we drive along Skirsa Street in Cadder, the next flurry of snow arrives covering the freezing flakes below, whilst reassuring Hughie that the brief but steep incline up Fara Street will not induce a skid by the hearse into the kerb, or worse, a parked car next to the kerb. That's the thing about hearses and limousines, being modified vehicles, usually stretched and re-welded, for road traction in icy weather, one needs lots of weight in the back for stability, and fortunately, with a heavy coffin on the deck of the hearse, we do have traction and glide slowly, and successfully up Fara Street to Tresta Road.

The limousine behind us is not so lucky, and due to there being only three passengers in the back seats, it struggles and skids its way up the slope, eventually making it after a few minutes by clinging to the kerb side where previous vehicle wheels have not compacted the snow into sheet ice.

We proceed tentatively across Tresta Road into the St Kentigerns section of the Western Necropolis and proceed slowly, following the cemetery supervisor, with his orange warning light flashing on the roof of a green district council parks department pickup, towards the opened grave. In front of us we see a large estate car has slid off of the road and is now resting near a neat row of gravestones. "Lucky that car didn't hit the stones, knocking them over. I bet that's happened a few times in the past on days like this!" I quip to Hughie. He says nothing, focussing instead to keep the hearse on the track.

"Looks like the clergy car," I add, squinting at the vehicle, and feeling glad that it is not stuck on the road, and getting in our way. Further ahead the supervisor's pickup starts to skid turning a tight corner, almost loosing traction, but not quite. The hearse arrives at the corner and instead of turning, slides gently off the track and towards some old gravestones standing upright down a gentle slope.

We stop as we hit the first of the stones, feeling the crunch of metal against granite, and watching silently as the stone, standing four feet tall, topples, stopping with a dull thud and flurry of snowflakes as it hits the ground. "Fuck!" spits Hughie. "I will have to report this."

59

I sit silently, thinking only about that fact that we will now have to carry the coffin, along with the flowers to the grave side, and with the ground the way it is, it will be hazardous. The limousine drifts past us, still on the road and stops about ten metres ahead, where the ground has been opened for the internment. I breathe a sigh of relief, so at least the grave is a lot nearer than I thought.

Because we must, we proceed with as much dignity as possible, the clergyman keeping the committal as brief as possible, much to everyone's appreciation. I approach the main mourner and apologise for the hearse sliding off the road. "Don't you worry son," she says, "It was snowing badly last time we were here, and it's an omen."

I never get to discover if the 'omen' is good or bad, but with the help of the council van and a tow rope, we dislodge the hearse from the snow-covered grass and navigate back out of the cemetery to the greater reliability of the public roads, which now have received their first generous sprinkle of road salt from a passing spreader-truck, doing its rounds and reassuring road users.

Back in the office I complete a report for John Farrell who huffs and puffs as he reads it slowly to himself. "Did the family complain" he demands to know. "No," I reply, "They understood the situation and thought it made the burial more memorable."

He sniffs officiously, "There will be an inquiry and disciplinary you know, after all there has been *negligence*". I hear him patiently out, then head up the road to the garage where everyone is now looking, chatting and opining about the sizeable scratched dent in the side of the hearse. "That can be T-cutted out with a bit of time and patience," chips in one part-time driver, but I don't think anyone agrees with him. Manny, the garage manager just rolls his eyes and affirms that in his opinion the hearse can be easily repaired, and, if there is no lasting damage to the stone it can be upended again and no one will be bothered. The drivers agree

Chapter Five - 1st fight at the Cemetery & sad silence in an empty flat.

So, there will be a formal disciplinary investigation I am informed, and 'heads will roll'.

I don't think I have done anything wrong, after all it was an accident, but that doesn't seem to matter. John Farrell, has rolled out of his office chair and into the general office to hand me a letter confirming that I am due to attend an 'investigative' meeting after complaints were received. I go up to the garage in Scotland Street and show my letter, unsigned and undated, to the shop steward, Ian Waddell, a small, sharp, canny and irritable man who has a taste for confrontation.

He arranges a meeting with Mr Dick, the Operations Manager, to examine the evidence. After some delay and repeated cancellations, the 'evidence' meeting happens. The shop-steward is the first to point out that it was an accident and that fortunately nobody was hurt. This is brushed aside by the Operations Manager, who insists that there must be 'accountability'. The Shop Steward responds as to why no road salt and a shovel are carried in hearses in winter to provision for such an eventuality.

The Operations Manager lifts a pencil, one of many sitting in a pen holder on his desk, and aggressively snaps it in two, throwing down the two left-over bits violently onto his desk. The Shop Steward asks if this is not a waste of company resources, to which the Operations Manager lifts a second pencil and snaps it in two, throwing the two pieces on the desk. The Shop Steward ask why the Glasgow City Council are allowing funerals to proceed in cemeteries with un-gritted roads, to which the Operations Manager replies that it is not relevant. The Shop Steward asks that, following company policy, will witness statements be sourced from all those involved in the event. The Operations Manager confirms that there will, after which the Shop Steward asks if this would include all the mourners and clergy attending the funeral. The Shop Steward asks to see the letters of complaint, but none are forthcoming. The Shop Steward asks if 'complaint letters' actually exist in the first place.

The Operations Manager snaps another pencil in two.

The whole incident is thereafter concluded.

This type of situation seems to happen on a regular basis over the years. "The thing is son!" states Ian Waddell, the Shop Steward, "It's a very British situation where those who work have to manage, because those who manage don't bother to work". A bit sweeping, but generally he is quite right. This is Britain. It's not so 'Great' these days. The glory days of empire are long since gone and probably just as well.

A few months later and the weather is brightening up nicely, with summer on its way, and birds singing busily in the trees and bushes around the cities scruffy landscapes. I'm out on funerals again. 'Funeral Week' happens for a week-long duration, once every four weeks.

I'm on hearse two with little Ted, and we have a simple, direct burial to Lambhill Cemetery at the back of the Western Necropolis Extension. It is a glorious day and as we arrive the diggers are in a good mood, after all, the internment is the last one and as it's a small coffin, not much digging has been necessary.

John, the notably muscular, good-looking, blond-haired digger is, as usual, leaning on his favourite old-fashioned spade, getting admiring looks from the female mourners in attendance. He's a bit rough, but nobody cares, after all, it's what you would expect a sexy grave digger to look like. His grubby shirt is unbuttoned down to his lower chest, and he does not seem to care about it.

The clergyman, who is a Methodist minister, witters on for ten minutes about 'angels' and 'rebirth' and 'sitting with god' and 'rewards in heaven' . . . the usual stuff. None of the attendees seem that impressed as they are mostly young and with little memory of the orthodox protocols of their grand-uncles religion so it means nothing to them, but still seems appropriate as content of the committal that they are witnessing. It's all authentic gothic theatre, and they are actors on its stage, mostly dressed in black, to suit the moment. The minister waves his hand in the air as a blessing, then lifts a lump of compacted clay from the ground to sprinkle into the grave, and onto the coffin, however, it lands with a dull thud, unsprinkled onto the lid, and someone at the back of the cluster of mourners starts to giggle, only to be quickly 'shushed' by those around her. They quickly move away and back to their cars, having each placed a single flower into the grave, which is a lot less dramatic than the heavy lump of clay offered by the officiant.

John wanders across, grinning, and looking for a chat. Little Ted and I notice immediately that he is sporting a recently acquired black eye, carefully covered with cosmetics so as not to distress funeral attendees. "Been in a fight at the yard!" he cheerfully explains, "a real beauty too . . . plenty blood". Ted and I are all ears. "Had a union meeting, and Albert, you know, the big fat bastard, got gobby with me, so we took it outside to sort it out. A few punches and kicks, but all good fun," he grins.

As Ted and I head off back down the road in the hearse, Ted describes the last time John was caught brawling at a graveside a few years ago, with a dog walker who had just allowed his pet to shit in an opened grave and was refusing to retrieve the excrement.

"Honestly Ted," I shake my head. "You could write a book all about this stuff."

It is not until a few weeks later that we get the full story from Bill, the gentlemanly attendant at Glasgow Crematorium, situated just opposite the cemetery diggers yard, and the only independent witness to what happened. Apparently, there was a union meeting called for all six diggers, organized by the city council. The purpose of the meeting being designed to shift the diggers by agreement off of overtime payments to a fixed salary. Bonuses were being offered for those who would agree to the change and sign the contract. Albert was happy to sign, John was not, then it got a bit 'shouty' and confrontational, then the two of them took it outside into the yard where Albert promptly punched John hard in the face just as he was taking his jacket off, sending John tumbling to the ground.

As Albert, using the advantage of his size and weight went down to immobilise John by sitting on top of him to deliver a few more face punches, John brought up his steel toe-capped boot and delivered a groin kick to Albert which almost lifted him off the ground. With a howl of pain

63

Albert staggered back allowing John to get to his feet and rush him with a few wide swinging hooks which appeared to bounce off of the bigger man who shielded them successfully having trained as a boxer in his youth.

Big Albert re-launched his attack grabbing John in a bear hug and sending both of them back to the ground where they both struggled and writhed for a few unproductive moments until, with Albert tiring, John took advantage with his greater fitness, and stood up, holding down Albert whilst he placed a few more well-placed kicks to his head and legs. Bloodied and exhausted, both combatants slowed to a halt, whilst their colleagues silently observed proceedings from through the canteen window.

At this point, the union official suggested the rest jump in and that they both be separated and cleaned up so that the meeting could finish. Both the combatants were ushered into the kitchen to get washed, calmed, and to get a few sticking plasters applied.

The adversaries sort-of made up, although later on John assured Albert whilst they were in the process of digging another grave, that he would, if necessary, take his spade across Albert's neck so hard that an ambulance would not be needed. After all, with over one hundred thousand graves to choose from, where would the police know where to find Albert's body!

Nobody expects to find 'missing persons' in a cemetery, and the number of official exhumation orders required would make a search impossible. Albert got the hint and sort-of made up with John.

The diggers went onto a salary, and accepted a nominal compensation offer for loss of earning potential. As diggers retire or leave, they are not replaced.

It's not long before we are back at the Western Necropolis again with another burial in the Lambhill section. It happens that way, where you will not see a crematorium or a cemetery for months, even years, then suddenly, you have two, even three funerals taking place at a single venue for no obvious reason. It's cheeky, cheery John who is standing at the graveside again, grinning unashamedly at the hearse as we arrive.

"Any developments with that toppled stone from a while back John?" I ask, as the mourners decant slowly from their vehicles. "Yes," replies the digger, "You did us a favour hitting that stone as it reminded the office that more of these old Victorian stones need to be laid flat 'cos they are getting to be a hazard to the young kids trying to knock them over, for fun".

"What!" I exclaim, "you can't be serious John? Surely young kids are not just vandalising the place for kicks!"

"Yes, they are, and just last week a parent got a lawyer to demand compensation for their little bastard wean when he trapped his ankle under an old stone after his two mates pushed it over". John sighs, and heads over to the graveside to assist in the forthcoming internment. It transpires that some local kids have been checking out loose graves stones around the cemeteries, then, if they find loose ones, team-handedly rock them violently back and forth till they fall over. Some stones break into pieces when they hit the ground.

The cemetery authorities do not purse the kids for vandalism, but instead decree that all old metal-pegged stones, mainly larger stones from Victorian and Edwardian times, are to be 'wobble-tested' by cemetery staff, and if any stones wobble more than three degrees, they are to be upended and laid flat using a small tractor. Health And Safety is the priority, not accountability.

Some families, and members of the public superficially complain, but generally, little is said and the situation is accepted, although some families attending burials are unaware that their gravestone has been deliberately toppled, but the 'health and safety' of little vandals is the number one priority. And there you have it.

At the end of the service, having completed yet another mission of mercy, I head back down the road in the hearse, with old Hughie driving with dignity and precision. "Wee bastards should be made to pay for the damage they do, and their parents too." retorts Hughie. "No respect for others these days . . . and no respect for themselves," he concludes. I totally agree with him, he's right.

I'm really getting the hang of conducting funerals now, thanks to the sheer volume of jobs I've had to do in a relatively short space of time. I also find that I am spending a lot of time on the vans, doing deliveries to parlours for viewings, and removals from hospitals and nursing homes for preparations and coffinings. My first year in the job has been the busiest due to a prolonged influenza outbreak which has seriously stretched the resources we have available, and has exhausted the shifts of funeral staff who have mostly been working considerable amounts of overtime to help manage the situation.

At the end of the busy period, Mr Dick offers to reward his funeral directors by offering to buy a basic trouser press for the staff room, so everyone can look smarter for funerals. The shop steward, Ian Waddell, suggests that a small financial bonus would be far more useful for those supporting young families.

Mr Dick says no, absolutely not.

Ian Waddell suggests that Mr Dick shove his trouser press up his arse.

Mr Dick snaps another pencil.

All is calm and collected as I arrive at the Smiddy for a pint of No:3 and a wee single malt too, seeing as how I have had a busy week at work. The usuals who frequent this homely bar are where they usually sit, having their usual chat and usual drinks, after all, humans are notorious creatures of habit, especially when it comes to pleasure and socialising.

James is rather busy behind the bar this evening, and looking a little glum, not at all his usual affable self. I take a seat next to the ladies in the

66

corner and wait for them to commence the conversation. It does not take long. "Have you seen Sanny recently son?" asks Jessie, " . . . he's just not himself these days, looking washed-out and ill". I think about the last time I've seen Sanny, it's been a few months now since I went to his house again to buy a few more little bottles of discarded samples, which he seems to have a lot of. "Last saw him about six weeks ago, when I was round at his house to buy some stuff," I reply to a question.

Jessie's big buxom pal, Alice, who works at the whisky bottling plant in Shieldhall, shakes her head with concern. She is sitting next to Jessie with a large gin and tonic, loads of ice, and a small wedge of lemon, listening and observing and thinking. Over dressed, but understated, she exudes self-confidence and although very different to Jessie, they are the best of friends, and have been since primary school days.

"I think," she states, "That he is ill, and just not letting people know about it. Men's troubles, or cancer, or *personal* issues, or something!" she concludes. "I think your right Alice, he's just not himself these days, and totally out of character" muses Jessie. The two ladies look again at me for, perhaps, some further insight, but I have nothing more to add.

I like Sanny, despite his selfish, cussed character, he's authentic, and worked a hard job as a cooper for forty years, with little appreciation by his employer, but, that's life, and I'm not overly worried about him, unlike the ladies here at the Smiddy. I make my excuses to leave as I am quite tired after a busy day of lifting, laying and carrying.

The ladies make a few funnies about me heading off to find a cemetery to sleep in. I laugh and I head up to the bar to have a brief chat with James, and to ask him about Sanny. "Had to bar him again for aggressive behaviour, so you won't be seeing him for a few weeks," he informs me. Then, wanting to change the subject, James tells me a bit about his son who's now been doing the Thai boxing for three years, since he started getting bullied at school, and loves every second of it. I am reliably informed that he no longer gets bullied at school, and will be leaving soon, to find an apprenticeship somewhere . . . if he can.

I listen attentively, as James is always considerate and gentlemanly towards me, along with having a mischievous view of my new career. "Any jobs going at the Co-op undertakers?" he asks. "Not at the moment," I reply. "But would your boy really want a dead-end job like mine?"

James laughs loudly, then remembers suddenly, "There's a couple of bottles in the back for you ralfy," and he shuffles off to get them. When he returns a few seconds later, he has a discreet plastic carrier with two bottles of single malt therein, both wrapped in bubble plastic sheets, and looking magnificent. "That's from Bill at Auchentoshan, and you owe him £40". I hand over two £20 notes, lift the bag, and go to leave. "Where you off to with them then?" shouts Jessie from the corner of the bar.

"What, MORE bottles of whisky," gasps Alice. "Off to the crematorium for a wee heat, and a comforting drink" I reply, then quickly head out into the still evening air, and then I notice it's lighter now for the time of day, because summer is on its way.

———————————————

Alec and I have just delivered several coffins to a number of parlours around the east end of the city of Glasgow. On arriving at the Shettleston parlour, Nancy, the worldly-wise, and chain smoking branch receptionist, slides me a note across her office desk. "That's a wee job for yous' son from they bastards down in Paisley Road."

Nancy is a single lady with a singular personality, like marmite, people either love her or hate her, probably because she is strong willed and smart too. The locals love her because she is very good at her job. The hand written note states:

1.15pm – message received from H/O
Police Shell
Respond immediately
200 Kirknewton Street
Male
Unidentified

To go to City Mort:

immediately.

Police require fast response.

I show the note to Alec, and with a wave to Nancy, who is now lighting up another cigarette behind her desk, we leave the parlour, jump into the van and head round to Kirknewton Street which is no more than five minutes away. Kirknewton Street is a cul de sac, a separated place, a row of residential modern flats and very quiet. Passing traffic is negligible as the street runs parallel to a main commuter railway line and is surrounded by mature green trees which add to the sense of suburban detachment and gentility.

We can tell immediately which flat we are looking for as a police car is parked outside and a mature police officer is standing on the pavement, waiting to lead us in. Alec gives him a wave of recognition.

Whilst Alec chats amicably to the officer, I retrieve the folding stretcher from the back of the van and we make our way inside an anonymous looking block which looks like most of the residents are elderly. It is neat, tidy and obviously looked after.

Three floors up, at the top of the landing, a very young and immaculately dressed policeman demands to know where we have been, and that we should be aware that we have a contract which states that response time is within 30 minutes. Alec pauses, looking enquiringly at the more experienced officer standing next to him. "We have just received notice ten minutes ago officer," Alec states, showing the hand written notice to the nippy policeman. "You will see that the time on the notice says ten minutes ago, which is when we were actually aware of your request."

The young officer tuts sarcastically, nodding his head and gesturing us into the flat. The front door has recently been smashed in, with splinters of wood laying on the ground. Inside, the flat is bare of furniture, furnishings, and fixtures . . . completely bare of anything. An old kettle, a chipped mug and a bowl with a box of cornflakes are all that can be seen in the kitchen. The place reeks of minimalist poverty and settled dust.

Alec and I are gestured by the young policeman towards the bathroom where, laying in the bath, a corpse lays grey and cold, a young man, naked, except for a small hypodermic syringe sticking out of his left arm, the needle still inserted where he administered his own lethal dose. No more than fifteen or sixteen, he has been a handsome young man with his life ahead of him, but none of that matters now, he has no future, his journey in life has been short and has ended abruptly, here in this place, in silence.

I can feel the tragedy fill the house,

I can feel the shock of the situation.

Outside, the birds are silent in the trees.

No birds are singing.

Not one.

Suddenly, the young constable breaks the silence which has manifested for no more than about five seconds. "Well then," he demands, "What are you actually here for?"

Alec and I pass each other a knowing glance, which does not go unnoticed by the older officer who is standing back in the corridor. Whilst the young constable huffs and tuts, Alec and I unfold the stretcher and place it on the floor beside the bath. I lay out a sheet of white plastic on top of the stretcher, and with Alec at the head and myself at the feet we slowly remove the young lad from out of the bath. Once secured with retaining straps we carefully manoeuvre the stretcher out of the empty flat and down the stairs to the van outside.

On the first floor, an old woman opens her front door, and with tears in her eyes blows a kiss towards the boy we are carrying. Immediately on seeing her, the young constable shouts at the old woman, "Get back inside madam!"

Once outside on the roadway, and with the stretcher secured inside the van, the young constable states that he will be driving the police car to the city mortuary, and that we are to follow him closely, and not to leave his sight. The older officer opts to travel with Alec and myself inside of the van. We head off, rather rapidly, out onto Cockenzie Street, and head speedily down Shettleston Road after the police car.

The older police officer, sighs, "So how are you doing these days Alec?" he asks.

"Fine," replies Alec. "Although I do get the impression Marty that you are looking forward to retirement next month". Officer Marty sighs again. "You know," he states, "With little cunts like my junior colleague there, full of attitude and ambitions, I'm just glad to be getting out now before I give someone like him a proper slap. I just don't know what is possessing the top brass, with promoting these degree holding pricks, full of attitude and dangerous immaturity . . . honestly, it's no wonder it's getting harder for the public to trust police these days, they have good reason not to, very good reason."

Alec laughs, "Aye Marty," he says, "You're probably right, and anyway, before we get to the mortuary, how come I've no seen you down the Club over the last few months?" "Work," replies the older officer, "Constant overtime, with my lieu days being stacked up to allow me to get out that bit sooner . . . and the sooner the better". The van goes silent for a few seconds. Alec goes quiet and then attempts to change the subject by commenting on the tragedy of the young man laying in the back. "The usual," spits Marty. "War on drugs, fuckin' war on drugs . . . my arse. That poor wee bastard in the back of your van never did anyone any harm, I've known that lad for years now, quiet, thoughtful and far too trusting for his own good, and that's how they got him . . . trust!"

"And look where he's going now, the city morgue for a post mortem then a basic funeral with only his mum and wee brother likely to be attending. It is just tragic, and the public just don't want to know, just keeping their blindfolds on and reading the papers. The war is WITH drugs, not ON drugs, and the State provides them, profits from them, and the vulnerable ones use them, then die . . . If it wasn't for the kindness of his elderly neighbours making him meals, this young lad would have been away last year. It makes me sick the way society accepts it and denies the cull taking place, and I'm glad to be getting away from it in a few months."

Alec nods knowingly, and we arrive at the city mortuary with the young constable standing, irritated at the top of the steps at the entrance. "What kept you then?" he demands, without bothering to wait for a reply.

On the road back to the main office, Alec explains how the job opens up some very different perspectives on society, and how people don't actually want to see things as they are, only as they want to see them. It's real life, and it's just the way it is. People don't want 'real' freedom, which means responsibility, making good use of time, being self-reliant, no, people want donuts, pizza, football, upgrades and movies, that's what freedom means to most people, and to just believe everything they are told on telly, and in the papers, and from soulless people in suits and ties.

"Has this job changed your life much Alec?" I ask. "A lot more than I would ever have realised." he replies, quietly.

Two weeks later, and I am driving the hearse for a change, a spare one. Not the usual model Daimler Benz, but a loaned Volvo from a peripheral branch of the Co-op, where expectations of vehicles are more modest within the community. It's a lovely vehicle to drive, and with heated seats, which are not so much of a novelty as it is summertime, but I try them for warmth anyway. Super cosy! I quickly switch off the heated seats button.

The funeral is for the young man I lifted out of the bath with the needle still in his arm from two weeks ago. It's a simple funeral, paid for by the social services department of Glasgow Town Council, who provide this service to ensure that nobody is ever left waiting in a mortuary for need of a funeral service. A local Presbyterian minister is officiating, and despite meeting with the mother and young brother, has very little bespoke content to pad out the eulogy.

My esteemed and highly eccentric colleague Boaby Gray is conducting the funeral, and I am there to drive, and to observe . . . so that I learn something, maybe. Boaby is a squat, lumpy man, with a robust physical frame, a cheery sense of humour and a very large head over which a comb-over glue-down of sandy hair strands makes him look like a big pink coconut.

Both affable and odd, Boaby is a keen gun owner, and a regular at his local gun club at a time when such activities are still allowed. He owns four hand guns, but in a few years' time, under the Snowdrop Campaign Appeal, he will sell them to the government for a considerable amount of money. The Snowdrop Campaign Appeal will be considered a success in the media, despite public rumours.

We drive slowly through the gates of Glasgow Crematorium, considered a more discreet venue, and away from the deceaseds community, where he can quietly disappear forever with only his mother, younger brother, and a neighbour as witness. The Service is awkward, and silent, with the sympathetic words of the clergyman ignored by the mourners. There is an attempt at a hymn after the committal, 'Abide With Me' seemingly suitable, but only the clergy sings two verses of the hymn. The mourners remain silent. There are no flowers, no additional music, no tears, no reception after, no nothing.

The mother, a woman, poorly dressed and in her mid-forties, comes up to the hearse to thank Boaby for his services. He smiles, and then reassures her that she must get on with her life now. I would not have known what to say, but I would not have said that, it just seems a little harsh, uncomforting, blunt, but Boaby is a basic sort of man, and direct with his words, and anyway, what can one say in such circumstances. Probably to say nothing is best.

The mourners head off, walking down to the main road in Cadder to find a bus to take them back to Shettleston, and we nod to the minister who is not looking very happy as he has not been paid money by the family as a 'minding'. Clergy expect to be paid; after all, they are professional people.

Boaby, myself and the Volvo hearse head back down the road, the hearse still occupied by the memory of the funeral held ten minutes previously. I ask Boaby what he thinks of the situation we have just left. He pauses, thinking deeply for a minute before answering. "I think life is shit for everyone, just more for some and less for others." We head by the Maryhill Road parlour for a cup of tea and a smoke. There is no rush to return to Paisley Road office, they will not be expecting us for at least another half hour.

A complaint has been lodged with the regional manager Mr Dick. A police inspectors complaint no less, and I am to be disciplined, possibly demoted to 'funeral service operative'. It is the young police constable from the flat removal Alec and I attended to three weeks ago. He is claiming that Alec and I were 'unprofessional' and not 'following his directives'. He says I called him 'charlie'! It's all very odd. Ian Waddell, shop steward is called into the manager's office. 'Heads will have to roll' he is informed. "Fine," he replies across the manager's desk, "So long as Co-operative policy is adhered to, so I will need to see all witness statements."

A pencil is snapped.

The young police officer refuses to provide a statement as it may not look good for promotional prospects, and a manager has been assured, on speaking to the police inspector, that 'a glittering career awaits this talented young officer with the right attitude and ambition'. Somehow, I don't doubt that for a minute.

I ask Alec to pass on a message to Marty when he sees him next, 'to wish all the best for his retirement'.

His retirement timing has been good.

Chapter Six - Crisis at the crematorium & decaying shrines & Stuck in a lift.

"How can they *bastards* even sleep at night?"

I am suddenly startled from out of my slumber, sitting on a bus seat, the number 6 from the city centre, travelling west along Dumbarton Road. An upset old woman is sitting in front of me and has turned round to provide her opinion.

"Look at them!" she points. "Spooky creepy bastards laughing and grinnin' and eating hot pies outa' Greggs."

I rub my eyes to remove the sleepy blur and look out of the bus window at the three men now exiting Greggs the bakers and walking swiftly back to Robertsons Funeral Parlour in Heyburn Street. "Gives you the creeps, so it does, to think o' them *handling* you when you're dead, . . . with their greasy hands". I murmer a soft mumble of nothing in reply, and sink back into the bus seat, trying not to laugh out loud. I start to laugh out loud. The wee old woman looks at me, alarmed and suspicious. I explain that 'I'm on medication from the doctor', before getting up out of my seat and exiting the bus at the next stop. I will have to walk half a mile yet to reach my destination, but I don't care.

I am still laughing the following day when, back at work. I tell the guys who were in buying their pies what was said on the bus. They laugh too. We find it hilarious.

I have reported to Mr Robert Smith, Superintendent at Glasgow Crematorium, that some of the front stairs of his crematorium are looking a bit 'crumbly'. He says it's due to frost damage, and will be repaired. The repairs fail to materialise over the next few months, but suddenly I take a tumble on a damaged step, falling flat on my face, smashing my front teeth in, blood everywhere, followed by a damaged coffin, a rush of activity, and me left sitting on the steps, blood turning my white shirt to red, as what remains of the foot of the coffin is manhandled with as much dignity as possible into the chapel, . . . and me still left sitting on the steps.

Well, what a fuss.

Hughie the hearse driver takes me immediately to Stobhill hospital, where a junior doctor, . . . or a nurse, . . . I can't quite remember now, stitches my inner and outer upper lip where a massive bruise is manifesting over the right side of my face. I am then driven back to the head office to complete an incident report, and to change into a new shirt before taking over some paperwork processing in the general office.

John Farrell tuts with exasperation. "Would you say what you did was negligence?" he demands to know. "No." I reply, but this does not seem to impress my sweating and uncomfortable boss who is clearly looking for a quick blame to make things easy. There is to be a disciplinary enquiry. Heads will roll.

The protracted enquiry eventually concludes, after receiving photographs taken of the steps at the crematorium, that it's best to just quietly drop the case.

A month later I am summoned by Mr Dick the regional manager, into his office. He is laying back comfily in his padded chair, it has upholstered arm rests, as befits his status. He lifts a pencil and taps it noisily onto his desk, thinks, and laughs coldly, then offers a cheque towards me for £60 which is half of my recent dental bills which were required to repair my face after the fall. I say 'thank you'. He sighs and pauses, whilst staring out of his window, then after about ten seconds gestures me to leave his office. I think he must be going soft these days. I am advised later that the personnel department advised him to do it to avoid legalities and potential breech of company policy.

———————————————————————

Summer has been and gone. The warm winds of August are now tinged with the damp and chill of November and colder rain is on its way. Nights are drawing in and I have a removal tonight, at 7pm into St Benedicts Catholic Church in Easterhouse.

The day has been a long one with a lot of lifting and carrying around hospitals and parlours with the van, and I am feeling washed-out by the end of it. I notice that one of the funeral service operatives called 'bloomin Gerry' is my hearse driver. No luck there, he is a scatter-brain and not very organised, however, the show must go on, and I sit down with him in the staffroom at Scotland Street to discuss the evenings removal.

The coffin is currently at the deceased's home in Westerhouse Road, a first floor flat. It was taken home the day before and my two colleagues who attended to this were hard-pushed to get any help from the family. The trouble with coffins in houses is not so much the lifting, it's the twisting and turning around corners and up or down narrow stairs. Even a light coffin can encounter difficulties of manoeuvring within small-space modern homes which are designed to be smaller, flimsier units for bigger, fatter people. I blame the modern diet and increased material wealth along with the desire by house building businesses to extract greater profit from inferior built homes, which buyers blindly accept.

The flat we are going to is certainly not the worst; however, I suspect, from enquiries with the parlour receptionist, Nancy, at Shettleston Road, that the family members tonight will be drunk. We arrive at the flat at 6.30pm, having driven though heavy commuter traffic, and yes, the rain is now on, and getting heavier. I ascend the close stairs with Gerry in my wake, and greet the main mourner, the deceaseds wife, but then realise that she is too upset and drunk to talk to, so I speak instead to her daughter, who is still sober, and then discover that we have about 18 assorted floral arrangements to take down to the hearse.

Gerry and I transfer the flowers as quickly and as carefully as possible, but soon notice some flowers have been lifted and then dropped and damaged within the house before we arrived. These things happen. We ask for help from mourners and they rapidly volunteer making the passage of flowers to hearse easier. The sober daughter then informs me that family members will be carrying the coffin at all times.

Gerry and I firstly close the opened coffin, extinguishing the candle flames on the alter set, and then usher the six young bearers into the room and line them up around the coffin, according to height. I recommend that we will proceed down the outside stairs carrying at waist height, hands under the coffin, then once outside in the garden, we will lift up onto their shoulders before making our way to the waiting hearse. They mumble that they understand the instruction then, with a lot of grunting, shuffling and getting stuck at the front door, we proceed down the stairs, myself at the front, and Gerry at the rear. All goes well until we get outside and the bearers now have the coffin on their shoulders. Just as we are about to move towards the hearse, an old man with a walking stick rushes forward and lifting his stick, places the curved handle around the neck of one of the younger bearers and pulls him violently away from the coffin. As the young bearer is reluctant to let go of the coffin, he pulls it with him, forcing the rest of the bearers off the pathway and onto the wet and slippy grass next to a thick privet hedge.

There is a cry of anguish from the assembled ladies, and curses from the men. The old man, the deceaseds brother, is pulled away and his cane is quickly confiscated. Another two bearers kick-off, and with a shouting match commencing, lunge towards the old man to give him a smack. The remaining bearers lurch towards the hedge, swiftly depositing the coffin within the twigs and branches where it comes to rest, half way down inside the bushes, whilst they rush to stop a fight happening.

It's too late.

A fight breaks out.

I immediately caution Gerry away from the flying fists, and we withdraw ourselves out onto the road beside the hearse. "Should I move the hearse in case it gets damaged?" asks Gerry. "No, " I say, "Just leave it, so long as they remain fighting in the garden. If the fight spills out onto the road, then you can move the hearse to save it."

However, the crisis is suddenly over after about twenty seconds as the widow screams out for everyone to stop as the priest will be waiting . . . and the family must not be late.

The daughter takes over, ushering the bearers back towards the coffin, still laying, swaying gently, side to side within the hedge and it is soon removed and placed, visibly scratched, into the hearse. We proceed down the road to the church, where the priest is standing waiting at the door, with the pass-keeper squinting from behind the crucifix he carries, reassuring the priest that they should not be waiting much longer. The old priest is a gentleman, surveying the scene before him knowingly and quickly blessing the coffin with holy water before leading us down to the alter where we assist the family in depositing the coffin, facing the alter, onto the waiting wooden trestles. Gerry and I attend to covering the coffin with an expansive unfolded white pall cloth before bowing towards the alter and retiring discreetly from the building as the priest continues his reception.

Back out in the hearse, Gerry lights a cigarette, coughing and still agitated at the excitement of what we have just witnessed. I crouch down into the expansive leather seat and tell Gerry to 'just get us out of here' and, with the roads a bit quieter now, we return rapidly along the M8 motorway to the Scotland Street garage. I get home around 9pm, having completed a brief report on the incident for managers. I sit in my kitchen in silence, absorbing the ripples of the evenings drama.

With this job, surreal experiences and dramas are never far away, and I can feel happenings like this changing my outlook on life . . . changing my reality. A whisky is poured, Laphroaig, but not too much, because I have noticed earlier that funeral work has been changed again in the office, and I, along with Hughie on hearse number one, will be conducting the funeral tomorrow, from St Benedict in Easterhouse, to the Western Necropolis Lambhill extension cemetery. The weather forecast is for blustery winds and heavy rain, which should keep people's attention away from the scratches around the sides of the coffin.

I am sitting in the Smiddy, quietly in the corner absorbing the news, just relayed by James the barman . . . that Sanny is dead. He died at home, alone in his garage, whilst drawing a bright sunny countryside picture with crayons and pastels. The picture has since been burnt by his wife Ella.

My pint of No:3 sits untouched beside a small wine glass with a double of Bunnahabhain 12yo in it. James calls me from the bar, holding a small jug of water for the dram. I go up to collect it. "So will you be doing the funeral?" enquires James, ". . . after all, it is from your parlour in Hayburn Street. The Co-op does own Robertsons, doesn't it?"

"Yes," I reply flatly, now thinking of every way to avoid conducting Sanny's funeral. The thing is, I live in this community, and the more I'm seen in a professional capacity, the more subliminal barriers arise. The 'undertaker' is only ever a separate part of a community that a person serves. One is forever attached to the worst day of everybody's life, and that has its impact on social relations.

It's just the way it is.

It never changes,

ever.

I think about Sanny, cantankerous, opinionated, angry, singular, and of course, the instigator of the introduction to my whisky journey, in conjunction with the Smiddy bar itself. I don't feel sad, or any sort of upset, and certainly no obligation to spout condolences and sympathy about how marvellous a man he was. That would just be fake, and as a result of my job, I see far too many people being fake. Some a little fake, with genuine intent, and others a lot of fake, with wilful ignorance and drama.

The funeral is arranged at the parlour with Moira Glass, a tousle-haired, dishevelled, but polite and sympathetic receptioniust, being educated, practical, and the fond owner of an old green Skoda Estelle, which we find fascinating because on cold winter days it requires starting with a crank handle, stuck through a gap in the fender under the front bonnet. Moira is a character, a talented teacher or an accomplished academic who has missed her role in life and ended up arranging funerals in a small, wood-panelled, split-level shop front masquerading as a proper funeral parlour.

If I have the time, I always chat with Moira in the parlour as our conversations are authentic, original, and priceless. She is a wonderful human.

The families who come to her for arrangements like her too. Well, all except Sannys wife, Ella, who grumbles about the costs, and demands tea and a biscuit when she calls in to arrange Sannys funeral. "I want a wide coffin, mind, so he's not all scrunched up in the box!" insists Ella. Moira duly makes a note of this request and concludes arrangements as quickly as possible. It does not take long. It's kept simple and cheap.

I attend as a mourner on the day of the funeral.

Direct from Robertsons Parlour to Clydebank Crematorium, North Dalnotter.

The cortege creeps slowly along Dumbarton Road towards Clydebank until turning right up a steep hill called Mountblow Road. On the left lies Auchentoshan Distillery, with its elegant cooling pond feeding a large ornamental fountain, surrounded by low-laying whitewashed old buildings looking every bit the proper place for making scotch whisky.

I'm not such a fan of Auchentoshan, it is often a good malt badly presented which dulls its dynamic elegance.

The service and committal in the modern but characterless crematorium becomes memorable when James agrees to say a few words about Sanny whilst standing at the catafalque with the coffin just behind him. The few mourners attending are surprised to hear a lot more about Sanny than they were originally aware of. Ella had allowed James a few words, but clearly did not expect him to be so informative. Sanny was an ex-military man, an N.C.O. in the army logistics corp. There he excelled in organisational leadership, then, on early discharge for reasons never disclosed, he trained as a cooper at the warehouses of a large scotch whisky manufacturer. He was good at his job, and never once had a day off sick. He was not the type for sick days. He was a local champion at darts tournaments, snooker and fond of chess too. His poetry was never published, but a local university approached him once to supply some of his writings to an exhibition, but he never gave anything over, it was simply not his style to do so. He drew well in pencil, crayon and pastels, sometimes using gouache for colouring. He was a nonconformist, and contrarian, and it suited him well.

Back at the Smiddy, some sandwiches were laid out across the bar, along with small pork pies and nibbles. Ella left after thirty minutes to get a bus back home. James kept things ticking over for the funeral guests and a few early regulars till it got busier, then he cleared his bar and mourners wandered off into Dumbarton Road for shopping and fresh air. I left early to get back to work.

"And where have you been all this time?" barks John Farrell on my return to Paisley Road. "At a friend's funeral!" I reply, surprised by his tone. "Well, you've been away too long, and were getting stuffed with jobs," he retorts. "Go and get this arrangement done!"

I take the arrangement sheet, and phone the family to check the address and to give a time of arrival. The family are confused, they are going to the local parlour and don't know why I am heading out to their house. I write the update in red pen onto the arrangement notice and hand it back to John. He turns red and huffily demands that I remain in the office processing funeral arrangement forms. I think he really hates me now.

I ask Hughie and Alec about John's animosity, to get their opinion. "Just ignore the idiot," suggests Hughie. "He probably sees you as a future threat to his position Ralf, seeing as you are manager material, and he's not doing a competent job," opines Alec. Alec is probably right. I finally decide to just ignore John. It makes him worse.

I remain in the office for the rest of the day, processing funeral arrangements over the phone with various parlour colleagues scattered around the city in their rather shabby hubs, most of which are in need of an upgrade to make the venues a bit more inviting for families. One thing that always fascinates me is the complete absence of hot running water from the taps of the toilets at these venues. Most parlours have one single toilet, which is always the coldest room on the premises. They have a stark, soviet look to them, with a basic clay sink, usually too small for practicality, along with a basic lavatory, always slightly grubby, and with a plain black plastic seat. A bottle of liquid hand soap rests beside the sink taps, one of which delivers cold water, and the other, non-functional. Virtually none are convenient for wheelchair access.

I find the soaps to be of interest due to the fact that they are bought from the parlours petty cash which means that they are the individual scented choice of the parlour receptionists. Around all thirty-odd parlours within the region, no two soaps are ever the same, and the choice of smells never ceases to amaze me, in fact, I eventually ask about the choice of soap with the parlour staff. Some are chosen simply as they are on a discount deal, buy two and get three etc. whilst others reflect the preferences of the individual buying them.

Light, floral scents are popular, 'lily of the valley', 'honeysuckle', 'snowdrop', and 'vanilla', in the south of the city, whilst more fruity scents like 'mandarin, 'lime & lemon', 'orange crush', and 'red cherry', dominate the east and north of the city. In the west of the city, the parlours tend to go for 'bergamot', 'basil', and 'rosemary', which tend to be the smells of soap I prefer myself. Rather strange, I know, what with all the daily dramas of the job over the years, but I remember so much about intense chemical scents from liquid soaps in cold, miserable, unwelcoming funeral parlour toilets. Odd, don't you think?

Tonight, at 6.30pm, I have another removal into church as part of my late shift. This time it is St Aloysious in Rose Street, Garnethill. I love this church because it is traditional, festooned in exotic marble inlay, it has a great classical atmosphere, and also, the priests are 'brand new', and never any hassle. Most Catholic Church removals for reception and vigils are quite straight forward. Families are generally fine. Priests are generally appreciative. But sometimes things go a little 'wayward'.

This happens one wet, dark and windy night in December, just before Christmas, when I uplift the usual work sheet for the job, and proceeded with my hearse driver towards the low blocks in Cowcaddens, Dundasvale Road. To be precise, to a second floor flat in a large, monotone grey cement tower block, looking as dismal as I make it sound. My affable hearse driver was the first to tell me about the problems getting the coffin home. In fact, driving the hearse is Billy Flannigan, thin, cheery, and prematurely greying, who was sent to assist at the maisonette as soon as the call came into head office that the coffin had got stuck on the stairs. This was a direct result of the fact that at the last minute, the widow had decided that instead of the open coffin remaining downstairs in the main room behind the front door, it had to go upstairs into a small bedroom so as to leave room in the main room downstairs for all the mourners coming to the house for a vigil and some 'decks of the rosary' before going up the road to church later that evening.

Problem was, the staircase was narrow and the coffin was wide, so, it simply got stuck, until finally, the widow was convinced to change her mind, and let the coffin remain, on trestles, in the downstairs room. She was not happy, and it did not help much when a helpful family member, trying to assist the funeral staff get the coffin upstairs described the deceased to her as a 'wee fatty'.

It took ten minutes to 'unstick' the coffin so as to avoid any damage, although one of the plastic cremation handles came off, but was discreetly wedged back on again without anyone seeing what was happening. It is one of the necessary skills of the job, the occasional 'wedging' on of disconnected handles. At least I am prepared for the worst. As we ascend in the clunky and dilapidated lift to the third floor, Billy leads me towards the house, which is easy to spot as about thirty people in black clothes are milling around outside in the walkway, being unable to get inside.

Billy and I elbow our way in politely, to meet a mountain of flowers surrounding the coffin. I quickly identified the main family, and arranged with them to requisition mourners to carry flowers downstairs to the hearse and to place the flowers by the side of the vehicle to avoid blocking access into the hearse for the coffin. At this point, six young men identify themselves as the bearers, and insist they will be carrying the deceased to the hearse. Billy and I look towards each other in agreement, as the bearers look both fit enough, and sober enough for the job.

The coffin is heavy, very heavy. After arranging for everyone to make their way down to the hearse, I am left with six bearers, one of the family to lock up and bring down the trestles, and both myself and Billy to supervise. As soon as we leave we have to stop after about ten yards as one of the bearers has left his inhaler in the house. He grabs his inhaler and returns, and then we move on, slowly, with several of the bearers clearly showing signs of discomfort. We stop again, laying out the trestles to put the coffin on, thus allowing the bearers a rest. We move on again, arriving at the lift, where the bearers agree amongst themselves that instead of going down the stairs with the coffin at waist height, we should just use the lift. I call the lift, and it creaks and rattles its way up to our level.

The lift door opens, the bearers shuffle in, discovering immediately, that the coffin will need to be stood up to fit. The deceased is tall . . . as well as being heavy. The bearers place the feet of the coffin down, and then one of the bearers finds a plastic gold handle in his hand, freshly levered from out of the coffin. There is an audible gasp from the assembled group but Billy jumps in and immediately reattaches the handle, subduing the stress of the situation. Now there are eight of us, plus the upended coffin in the lift. Billy presses to button for the ground floor. Nothing happens. "The lift can't take the weight, some of us will go downstairs!" exclaims a bearer. Three of them shoot out of the lift and disappear rapidly down the stairs. Five of us, plus the coffin remain, waiting patiently for the doors to close. With a grating of aluminium and steel, the doors shudder closed . . . then open again.

"Still too heavy for the lift," stutters another bearer, and after a quick agreement, the rest of the bearers head down the stairs leaving Billy and I alone in the lift with the upended coffin. With more metallic grating sounds, the door shudders close, and the lift remains where it is. "Shit!" I say to Billy, "Go down the stairs and get the bearers back, this lift is no' workin'." Billy speeds off down the stairs.

Suddenly, I am aware that someone with a shopping bag is shuffling towards the lift. What am I to do? Standing in a public lift holding an upended coffin is not a good look! I press the ground floor button. The door clunks and grates shut, and the lift does nothing. The lift door starts to open. Outside stands an old woman with her shopping bag, staring at me in astonishment. "Is that your coffin?" she asks. "Yes!" I reply, "I'm just taking it to my hearse." The old woman nods sagely. "That lift," she states, "Has a sticky switch, so you have to jump up and down to get it going."

"Thank you," I reply, and once I have let the door shut again, I start to bounce a little, whilst holding the upended coffin. There is a knock on the lift door. "You will have to jump higher than that, you know . . . a good HIGH jump," she shouts loudly through the lift door. I jump as high as I can, whilst holding the coffin as steady as possible, then suddenly, with a lurch, and much grinding of metal parts, the lift descends rapidly to the ground floor. The lift door grinds opens. Outside, about thirty mourners are looking at me, standing, embracing the upended coffin. I recover my wits, and call for the bearers. "You will have to wait a minute son," explains the widow. "The bearers have all gone upstairs to bring the coffin down."

When we arrive, late, at St Aloysious in Rose Street, we park the hearse at the side door in Hill Street. The priest ushers the mourners into the building whilst Billy organises the bearers again at the back of the hearse. Some family help out by carrying in the flowers which soon pile up in a side chapel as a mound of leaves and scentless clusters. The priest grins at me, "That sinking feeling," he chuckles. We proceed into church, and once our mission is complete, Billy drives me back to Scotland Street garage to complete an incident report form.

Back home, I have some dinner, and light the fire in the grate. With the coal soon flickering into yellow cosy flames I pour a whisky, drink it then pour another. It does not last long, and then I pour another. It lasts a bit longer, and then I pour another, which lasts me to the moment I tumble into bed and succumb to a night of deep and dreamless sleep.

At one point I awaken, in the depth of the night, to the faint sound of grating metal, like the sound a metal door would make, closing then opening again. It is faint and far away, possibly a delivery van or something, I don't know, but it spooks me. I eventually fall back to sleep and remember nothing until the alarm shocks me awake at 6.30am in the morning. It's another day, another drama, another theatre, in and around the city.

I look at my whisky glass, empty, and the reduced fill levels of a few whisky bottles standing like artworks by the fireside. I think I will need to watch what I'm drinking these days.

After all, a slow passion can become a hard habit.

Chapter Seven Goodbye James & meeting Anubis at the Temple

A lot is changing in the world.

The little world in which I am comfortable and which is my daily routine.

The little world of passing drams and dramas, private theatre, singular tragedies and hopes, with so many people passing through my days, garnishing the days with their provenance and situations.

Every one an individual circumstance but similar to others in the communities, and beyond.

Bad news has been suddenly announced. James, after more than eighteen years, is leaving the Smiddy and taking his small family to Thailand for a new beginning . . . for new family adventures.

None of the customers are happy about it.

Many of the regulars are keeping their disappointment quiet so as not to taint the leaving party, but one can just tell that with this seemingly 'little' change, a lot is changing. I make a point of dropping in on a quiet afternoon, about 2pm, to get a chat to James, and to wish him all the best before he leaves. After a few No:3's, I let it slip that I expect to leave the Smiddy behind after James is gone. He reassures me that nothing will change, which reinforces my belief that it will. We have a brief and fleeting exchange of awkward silence. It's the way life is. I pause to capture the warmth and silence of the near-empty bar, conclude my conversation with James, then head off home for tea and a dram by the fireside.

On the final night of James managing the bar, I arrive early, to get a seat, and to get my 'cherrio's' in whilst sober and with less fuss and attention. James has put a buffet on the bar, and refuses to charge us for the food. We present him with a bottle of Johnnie Walker Green Label, and wish him all the best, and then I join the ladies in the corner table for a chat.

Jessie is pished, and trying to look sober, which is quite amusing, especially when she tries to present herself as more 'proper' and doesn't succeed. Margaret my neighbour, sitting next to her is sober and restless as she is convinced that the Smiddy will not be the same. I agree with her, and we change the conversation.

Moira Glass from Robertsons funeral parlour down the road, sticks her head through the bar door, and on seeing Jessie, who has invited her, she finds a spare seat and joins us having sourced a large gin and tonic, with extra ice. I swiftly discover that they are all members of Charing Cross spiritualist church, and after downing her gin and tonic in seconds, Moira is keen to tell the table that a man named 'Alexander' has visited and messaged her in a recent spiritualist meeting to tell her he had been murdered by his wife.

All the ladies look glum at this news, and after a little persuasion, Moira is encouraged to change the subject. She is not a bar regular, preferring to drink at home, but knows Jessie from the Off Sales liquor shop out along the street. Margaret and Moira, along with Alice and my down-stairs neighbour Margaret meet regularly at a community club support group. Margaret confirms that it should be discussed further between them later on, when I am not around, after all, I am an undertaker, and we, according to most, are a different breed of human. I don't take offence, in fact, I like being different, it suits me.

The bar shuts at 11pm and the party-goers decant from the venue and off home to bed, or to consume more drink before going to bed. I go home for more drink too, whisky and water will do.

By a roaring fireside, I fall asleep, aided and abetted by seven large single malts and a pint of clear, cold water from the kitchen tap. When I awake the fire is low and smouldering a pale amber.

Orlando the orange cat smiles at me, then curls up to sleep at the side of the hearth.

It's happened before.

It will happen again.

It just happens.

Some smoke comes down the chimney, a brief flurry of soot, a mild backdraught from a passing blast of wind.

In a flurry of sand and dust, I am in a desert. Somewhere beside a small cluster of date palms and near a slow moving, dark-watered river snaking its way between huge rolling hills of fine golden sand. I am aware that there is a cold wind sighing contentedly over the calm and exotic landscape.

Some dogs bark passionately in the distance, where staccato points of lamp light from small square windows show the presence of a village. I am sitting on a small stump of a date tree, watching the stark reflections of a bright full moon cast ghostly veils of deep shadows and bright silver light over the land.

All is peaceful and calm.

I get up and walk up hill towards a huge stone edifice, and I know what it is because I have just been told by silent voices inside my head. In front of me is the temple of Kom Ombo, where Sobek the crocodile god lives.

All hail to Sobek . . . but it is not he who has summoned me here.

All hail to Horus, god of sun and sky . . . but it is not he who has summoned me here.

I arrive at the steps of the temple and within the silence and aromatic incense of the dim-lit halls I see the god Anubis, standing silently before an altar, blessing the air and sky, the land and water, the earth and air, the air and water. He is busy, and I understand not to interrupt, though I am curious to know why he has summoned me here.

Soon, he concludes his ceremony and strides across the temple floor to where I am lurking, half-hidden behind a statue of Bastet.

"Do you like being an undertaker?" he suddenly asks me.

"I think so, yes." I respond, respectfully.

"Fine," replies Anubis, "Then go away and get on with it!"

I pause briefly to look at this blue-haired upright creature, half dog, half human . . . all strange. His eyes are large and burn orange like a setting sun, and I am aware that his presence is important. I turn away and return back into a warm, dark room, familiar and functional, as I wake up from a very deep sleep.

There has been some soot come down the chimney and onto the hearth, so it's time to get the chimney cleaned.

Chapter Eight - Tatters of sentiment & an academic & a horrible woman.

Since I no longer go to the Smiddy due to the change in 'atmosphere' since James left, I have been drinking less beer, and more single malts along with water in the evenings, at home.

The change of pace suits me, and with such a rapidly growing collection of bottles, I am spoiled for choice.

I pop down the stairs to my neighbour Margaret occasionally, to share a more flavoursome dram with her and to catch up on the gossip of what the Smiddy regulars are up to now that no one seems to be still going to the bar. It has had a change of clientele and all the old regulars are gone.

Margaret has a growing appetite for single malts now, and buys Bunnahabhain from her pal Jessie along at the liquor shop. I pop in to the shop occasionally myself, but the selection of malts are very limited, so instead I find myself spending more time at Oddbins in Crow Road where I meet Andy, and as he's a big whisky fan, and from Islay.

We have easy and long conversations so long as the shop is not too busy.

I'm raising my awareness of more obscure malts like Rosebank, St Magdeline, Port Ellen and Brora, along with Glen Lochy, Millburn, North Port and Littlemill. I find bottlings amongst the Independent bottlers, visiting Cadenheads in Edinburgh on a regular basis to sample, chat and share the malt-moments with experienced and interested members of staff. I love to try all these obscure distillery bottlings, even if, on occasion, I don't actually like them.

Whisky is the perfect foil to my day job. It is the perfect distraction to the dramas of public service as an undertaker. I can remove myself from the challenges of a troubled community and the rawness of my job makes the whisky distractions all the more amicable and romantic. The whisky scene is romantic.

I do not know it yet, but I am generating a deeper interest in whisky just at the moment that general disinterest in whisky is coming to an end, and more and more people are finding their malt-mission. This sentiment creates Glasgows' Whisky Club, and it has only just been formed when myself and Andy from Oddbins turn up to be made welcome, and to try a few drams. It's funny how as one door closes in life, another one opens. Within weeks of me leaving the Smiddy for the last time, I find a new and deeper scene with the whisky club.

I never look back.

It's a grey and windy October day as we arrive, cortege in tow, at Lambhill extension cemetery for an internment of an infant. Cot death. It happens a lot more often than society admits. No official explanation is forthcoming as no evidence is conclusive as to the cause.

My thought is, examine the pharmaceutical medications the mother, and then the baby are being administered. Everything has a reason. Some reasons are convenient to deny by those in power. It's the way it is. Grieving families just have to move on . . . even if they don't succeed with moving on.

The diggers are looking a bit irritated as we arrive at the graveside. As I exit the hearse, a powerful blast of wind whips by the vehicles causing a racket as colourful plastic windmills whirr, fading plastic flowers whistle, rocking violently in their vases, and helium filled balloons with teddy bears and pink angels clatter and bang around small black and white generic memorial stones. The place looks like a small theme park that's just been hit with a tornado. Bright coloured plastic is everywhere, festooned across the cemetery and removing a sense of dignity and decency from the place. Now I know why the diggers are irritated.

"Some family started their shrine last year, then it caught on, and it's all gone downhill from there" says Albert, the big daft digger who now spends a lot of working time with his pal John. John is looking glum. "I've had enough of this; I need to get a new job. Management never back you

93

up, and the cemetery is turning into a pig sty. Just look at the place!" he concludes.

I can see they are right; the cemetery is becoming a dumping ground for sentiment and bereavement theatre. I don't mean to be harsh, but the litter and torn plastic filling the hedge at the edge of the cemetery is like a horizontal smear of colourful confetti.

As soon as the internment is concluded, the family place a barrier of small white plastic garden fencing around the grave, even before the diggers have a chance to back-fill it.

I finally see the mourners back to their cars after they conclude much hugging and smoking of cigarettes around the graveside. I am mindful not to rush them away, but another funeral cortege will be arriving in fifteen minutes with another infant. Child deaths seem to happen in spates for some reason, and I know there will be a reason, although this is never explained by the authorities. Society is not ready to examine this yet. The family are off to the pub for drinks now. Off to numb the pain of loss, and to socialise, to drink alcohol and to have another smoke.

I leave the cemetery with the sound of fiercely spinning plastic windmills, buffeted helium balloons bumping together like drums, and tattered sparkling, colourful plastic bits, smacking then colliding with anchored plastic flowers, now faded and discarded and waiting to go on a skip.

It is what it is.

I find that I'm really noticing more and more these days about the subtle qualities of single malt whiskies. Perhaps it's because I am now a member of Glasgows' Whisky Club, and so can talk to other whisky fans, learning from them and seeing whiskies through their own senses. The sharing of observations over individual whiskies allows the consensus of group perspective which is very useful for personal development.

Blind tastings and written notes for media reviews feature in the process of club membership, and regular hosted tastings by Industry representatives really amplify our collective knowledge and appreciation of malts.

My access to Industry professionals and to people who work in the Industry indirectly expands my view of the whisky world, and to what it means for the economy and culture of Scotland. Scotland needs whisky, especially whiskys internationally applauded reputation.

Many years later I will watch in horror as whisky maker after whisky maker damages this precious reputation through poor investment in casks, greed, and incompetence. It's a shame, and it's real life.

I begin to buy old whiskies at a local auction house, not that it has much of a reputation, but it is the only one specialising in whiskies, so I join the bidders and buy some faded, old, unwanted, nondescript pure malts, single malts, and blends. My Undertakers stash is growing. I count the bottles in the cupboard. There are nine hundred and ninety three sealed bottles. Out in the room, thirty five bottles are standing near the fireplace, all are opened, and very slowly the contents are being sipped and enjoyed.

At several moments over the years I contemplate becoming an alcoholic, however, I have to give up on it, as I just don't have the commitment, dedication and drive to be successful with this ambition.

———————————————

I'm in the office at Paisley Road, and I have just been handed an arrangement. I am to go to a house in the west-end of the city and attend to an academics funeral arrangement. As this sort of arrangement is simply not desirable to most of my colleagues, I have been selected to attend to it as I am a bit 'posh', being polite and unfazed by unusual requests.

As parking will be difficult, I take the underground train from West Street to Hillhead and walk down Byres Road to Ashton Road, just before the junction with University Avenue. I walk up the short flight of stone steps at number 11 Ashton Road and knock on the battleship grey front door. It is one of a fine old row of blond sandstone Victorian townhouses, and very opulent.

A young Slavic-looking lady opens the door and beckons me to enter without saying a word. She smiles a genuine and endearing smile towards me as I'm ushered into a back room on the ground floor where a large oak table dominates the space along with two tall-backed seats. Two of the four walls are floor to ceiling book cases, custom made, and stuffed with assorted obscure books, manuscripts and small replicas of ancient artefacts.

A man is standing by the back window, tall, old, rather shabby and seemingly affable. His short gray hair is neatly swept back over his forehead, and his beard and moustache are neatly trimmed and articulate his distinctive appearance. He is wearing a light gray shirt, buttoned up to the neck, and over it he sports a dark corduroy waistcoat with matching loose-fitting gray trousers. His brogues are dark, highly polished tan leather, and look expensive.

He introduces himself. "I'm Professor Norris, please sit down."

I pause to allow the professor to take first choice of seat. He sits down facing the window, towards the sun which scatters through the glass and onto the wooden parquet floor.

"Kaks teed palun Maria!" he calls to the young lady.

"Jah." she replies faintly, and soon I hear a kettle hissing in the kitchen.

"Breakfast or Earl Grey?" asks the Professor.

"Earl Grey." I respond.

"With lemon?"

"Yes please, but no sugar."

As the old man draws out a small bundle of scribbled notes from his trouser pocket, I arrange my folder opened on the table and survey a fresh blank arrangement sheet. "And what is the name of the deceased?" I ask. Briefly he looks confused, then smiles brightly, "Well, it's me actually, I want to arrange my own funeral, and hopefully will not be following up on it for at least six months". "Oh, sorry" I apologise, "my information is that someone else has just passed away". He laughs, "I'm not in any hurry, but

96

it is definitely me, I want to pre-arrange my own funeral". Maria arrives with the tea and a small plate of hobnob biscuits arranged tastefully on an ornate tray. "Aitah . . . thank you Maria!" says the academic.

Maria smiles, and leaves us, quietly closing the door to respect the professors privacy. "I have a blio glastoma, a brain tumour incubating slowly and steadily in my head young man, and don't want to leave a lot of fuss and bother to the university, so, I am making my own arrangements, simple, and practical," he slides back in his seat, seemingly glad to clarify the situation.

It is a simple arrangement, a cremation at Glasgow crematorium, a wicker basket coffin, a bouquet of seasonal flowers, nothing fancy, no limousines, direct, and with a Buddhist priest conducting the short service. The details are noted down within five minutes, it really is that quick.

Whilst he pours us some Earl Grey, I scan across his bookshelves, scrutinising the array of academic and philosophical hardbacks and paperbacks. "Mainly anthropological stuff," he interjects, "My subject for fifty years here at the department".

I'm curious, and he quickly registers my inquisitiveness.

I glance across his bookshelves at the array of obscure publications, wondering what knowledge lays there-in, curious as to how different that knowledge is to the indoctrinations of my schooling.

The professor registers my curiosity, and appears to make a decision within himself to break the set of academic orthodoxy and restraint.

Perhaps it's because he is dying, perhaps it's because he just wants to share some truths with an enquiring mind.

"You know young man," he continues, "There is so much more to the human condition than most people realise, and much valuable knowledge remains closeted within academic circles". My curiosity grows.

"Real human history is not what is taught in schools; otherwise the general population would be much more empowered by self-awareness."

He continues, warming to his subject, "The bible and many old manuscripts allude to a far richer and more dramatic history of the species, or should I say, *'collection'* of species, but for political reasons, a powerful elite would rather this knowledge never see the light of day. One of our purposes as academics is to censor and edit history on behalf of those who pay us and who endorse our careers".

I say nothing and just nod a little to affirm I am paying attention.

"Do you want to know more?" he asks politely.

"Yes," I reply.

"Humans did not evolve naturally out of Africa, that is an academic lie. Humans, of which there are several species are a hybrid adapted group of mammals genetically modified by extra-terrestrials who have inhabited this planet on and off for over a million years."

I listen in silence as the anthropologist drops his bombshell.

"It is clearly stated in the bible and other ancient writings, even after historical editing, that contemporary humans are a species with collective amnesia, especially when enforced through social censorship.

Imagine" continues the professor, "Discovering that the human collective is nothing more than a genetically adjusted ape species bred as a food-source for alien entities that can be barely perceived, and are certainly misunderstood."

I sit in silence, slightly stunned.

"Are you saying that humans are simply a food harvest to keep another species alive?" I ask. "Yes!" replies the academic, "They feed on fear and anger, and other negativities, whilst hiding their presence. Humans generate plenty of that sort of energy and we can now record it, examine it, and perceive the presence of the aliens, called *Anunaki* and *Jinn*."

I let the gravity of his comments sink in for a few seconds, and then ask myself silently and slowly if he is bluffing to get attention.

I decide after a further few moments of silence that he's not bluffing, but I find his views baffling and odd, but he really believes what he is saying, and there is probably plenty of evidence hidden away to back him up.

I finish my tea, as its cooling rapidly, and have a hobnob.

I hardly notice anyone on the train as I return to Paisley Road.

I am lost in thought.

The day is turning weird.

Could it be true?

Or just a big confusing bluff?

Once back in the office, I fax the 'Not Yet Dead' details across to the local parlour receptionist in Mansfield Street, who phones me immediately to say that she knows the professor from her night classes at the university over the last few years. Margaret, the receptionist is a gem, just a wonderful, honest and kind human being. Small, dark-haired and always simply dressed with no jewellery, she bares her burden of advancing multiple sclerosis and a dominating younger sister impacted by downs syndrome with the patience of a saint.

The night classes at the university are her one opportunity to get out, apart from regular visits to her local catholic church, St. Peters, in Hyndland Street.

I go over the arrangements with Margaret, but skip the after-talk, as I know it would only alarm her.

A few months later I spy Professor Norris one bright and sunny, summer's day as I'm walking up Byres Road on my way to the botanic gardens for a seat and a think. I give him a wave across the road, but even though he sees me, he does not seem to recognise me. I leave it be, I just know that he should not be disturbed. He does not look well.

I see Maria appear from out of a delicatessen and take him by the arm, guiding him carefully back to his house in Ashton Road. I ask Margaret about him, but she will only say that he is a conscientious and articulate tutor, appreciated by his students.

After he dies, I wonder . . . what will happen to all his books!

I have another arrangement the following day, and this one is very different. A south-side address, Giffnock . . . up-market.

I am told by a manager that I must be punctual as the family are very fussy.

I arrive in Barrland Drive five minutes before I'm due, to ensure that I fulfil expectations of the client.

The bungalow is small, neat and featureless, with a red brick mono block front area devoid of greenery. All the windows are draped in assorted net curtains to ensure privacy whilst allowing the occupants a clear view of their neighbours. I park the company car out in the road and proceed on foot to the front door, where the shiny brass doorbell provides resonant electronic Westminster chimes to alert the occupiers. I am left waiting for what seems like a full minute, and then just as I go to press the door chime again, the front door opens to reveal a gaunt, middle-aged woman dressed in conservative blouse and matching knee-length skirt, with an expensive lavender cashmere cardigan draped across her shoulders, unbuttoned.

"Well I suppose you had better come in then," she indicates dryly, stepping back and gesturing me into the house with her hand that holds a neatly folded cotton handkerchief. She glances suspiciously at my polished shoes. "You will wipe you footwear on the mat provided I trust?" "Of course," I reply, making sure I make a good show of wiping my shoes on the mat. "Kitchen," she states, walking me through to the back, where the spotless and expensive installation of lavender and cream fittings are fit for a magazine photo-shoot. I am gestured to a wicker chair. "My name is Amy Bransen-Bowes, and I am the next of kin". I nod, to register her identity, but say nothing.

I sit carefully on the edge of the seat, organising my arrangement folder to proceed as quickly as possible with the arrangements. I can easily sense the unfolding drama, and trouble brewing, but with several years' experience now, I have my way of dealing with people like this.

"Are you ready now mister man. I may as well call you mister man until you actually tell me your name!"

"Mr Mitchell." I reply, eventually.

I allow the silence to linger after my reply to her, there's no hurry, I will not be letting her set the pace. After about twenty seconds she relents.

"Now!" she says, "I want you to know my late mother was always known as Lettice, even though her name was Janice, and she was a very cherished person, and will be very sadly missed, and I have written you a funeral notice to go into the Herald and Times".

"Evening Times?" I ask politely. "Oh no!" she tutts, snorting in indignation.

"The National Times . . . London".

"Not a problem," I assure her, "We can arrange that."

She continues, "I have contacted my parish minister who will conduct a service at the Linn crematorium next Thursday at 2pm."

"I will have to check availability at the crematorium for that time," I insist.

"Already done, I have booked it personally . . . I have friends in the council." she concludes.

"And I will have to check on availability of a hearse and limousine if a car is required."

"Oh, whatever Mister Mitchell, just see that it gets done. I'm sure you can find a spare hearse from somewhere, just so long as it's clean and reliable."

I pause, staring at my folder, pen still on the arrangement sheet, re-appraising the individual I'm now dealing with.

This is becoming a whole new level of intense.

I keep my calm.

She is now striding up and down the kitchen, arms folded under her cashmere, lips pursed, looking for a weakness in me, something to criticise.

A neatly dressed and polite-looking old man pops his head in through the kitchen door, an empty white porcelain mug in his hand.

"Not now Jeremy, go and sit in the greenhouse till I'm finished."

He obeys immediately, disappearing across a manicured lawn towards some shrub roses and a glass house.

"I will be viewing the day after tomorrow at your little office in Paisley Road, and I want the room with the stain glass windows in it. I am not to be interrupted whilst viewing by any member of staff, and I want a kneeling prayer stool, padded, and a vase with water in it for the flowers I bring. I loved my mother very much you know, and she will be very sorely missed"

I nod and conclude the arrangements by noting down Mrs Bransen-Bowes detailed instructions as she stares over my shoulder to check I am properly noting her directives.

Back at the office, I get a cup of tea, just to clear my head after the intensity of the arrangement, and as I am doing this, Andy Barr walks into the kitchen grinning like a Cheshire cat. "Aye, son, you drew the short straw there, didn't you?" To this I reply, "So I take it Andy that you body-swerved this particular arrangement by shuffling the work schedule in the office!"

He just grins, and heads outside for another cigarette. The following day, Alec and I are out in the van, uplifting and delivering.

We have to attend a delayed removal from Nithsdale Lodge Nursing Home, Shields Road. Doctors have not completed paperwork for the cremation.

This is not an unusual situation.

It is a converted church, and looks opulent on the outside. Inside, though, fixtures and fittings are basic, and the smell of urine is hanging in the air. Staff seem flustered, always alert to the next criticism from whoever. We are directed to a tiny deceased old lady, in a single bed, somewhere at the back of the building, near a discreet exit.

Her name is Mrs Janice Bowes. Out of curiosity I ask the nurse if family has visited recently. "Never visited once in over two years." replies the carer.

"Just left some cards and photos at reception a few times, but did not want to see her mother going downhill, I suppose. Snooty sort of woman, full of herself. The old woman never got any visitors, it was such a shame, really, we were all the family she could relate to and such a quiet, nice old dear". I look across at Alec, who registers my anger.

Back in the van, I ask Alec, "Have you seen this happen much over the years?"

"Not that often," replies Alec sighing a little, "But when it does, you really never forget it."

The following day, Mrs Amy Bransen-Bowes arrives at reception around seven o'clock in the evening. She demands a glass of water, and then complains that the prayer stool is too low for kneeling. She complains that the flowers, forget-me nots and white lilies, are not fresh enough, and then complains that her late mother looks a bit pale. She demands that a member of staff knock the viewing room door at 8.30pm, and that a taxi be waiting at the front door to take her home. She lights a candle in the room, and insists that it be left to burn all night, to keep her beloved mother company, and so that she's not left in the dark.

On the day of the funeral, she complains that the second hymn at the crematorium is three verses too long. I watch as the limousine leaves at the end of the service. Amy and Jeremy are off back home to Barrland Drive, back to their bungalow and the mono block, back to green lawns and greenhouses, lavender kitchens and personal private-life dramas. I feel lucky, and make a note to pour a whisky later that night, back in the comforting solitude of my Partick flat, away from the madding crowd of decent people and indecent individuals, absurd in their reality, and often oblivious to their absurdities.

I ask Hughie the hearse driver about it the following week as we conduct a mercifully ordinary and humble funeral direct to the Linn Crematorium. As the service proceeds in the chapel, we walk around the back of the waiting room where it's quiet and discreet for such conversations. Hughie thinks for a few minutes then lights a cigarette.

"The way I see it," he says, "Some people go too far into their own world, and away from the real world, then get lost in their own private lives."

I think about his statement carefully, considering it for a minute "And then lose touch with reality I suppose!" I add.

"Yes." affirms Hughie, stubbing out what's left of his cigarette on a tree.

103

I change the conversation to what the Professor told me which leaves Hughie genuinely baffled, then in the distance we hear the doors of the chapel open signifying the end of the service. It has been a short service, no hymns, no eulogies, just some sincere farewell and all the more honest for it. Usually this is the best way to do things.

It's whisky night at Glasgow's Whisky Club, and I'm loving it. The thing about just sitting in a pub, chatting about whiskies is that you learn so much from other peoples experiences and opinions.

A few people from the whisky Industry have joined the club, out of genuine interest, and out of curiosity for what these new-fangled clubs might bring to the visibility of scotch whisky. Already, most conversation is around the subject of single malts, with only a few blends being mentioned with respect. Baillie Nicol Jarvie, also known as BNJ, and Black Bottle, along with Johnnie Walker Green Label get honourable mentions, but they are the few exceptions. Most blended whisky is regarded as pub mixing liquor, which is exactly what it is.

We are now getting some free bottles sent to us by distillers. These are portioned out on barrel nights, where about two dozen bottles are placed on an upended barrel and left for members to help themselves. Within about two hours, just by looking at fill levels, we can see which single malts are popular, and which are not.

The individual club sessions, which take place on a Wednesday evening, cost £10. Club membership starts to grow, and soon there are over thirty people included in the circle, with more enthusiasts queueing up to join in as soon as there is space. We have to limit the club to thirty members at any one time, just to keep things manageable. Also, with a 20mm pour, you get thirty measures out of a full, 70cl bottle of whisky, so it keeps thing practical to have a core group of 30 members.

One of the other clear advantages is that we can get to know each other better as there are not too many people which would result in relative anonymity within the group. There are the 'regulars' like Juliette, Jarkko, Bobby B . . . and myself, then there are the more recent arrivals, looking to find their feet, and make friends within the club whilst suppressing their amazement at the accessibility to good whisky at such a reasonable price.

Tonight is a regular club-meet at the Bon Accord, our new and very welcoming Club homebase. We sit through at the back of the pub, up in the mezzanine, only three steps up and allowing comfortable seating with tables. A few club members arrive early, including myself, to have a hot meal before the club officially starts, and this gives time for more informal chat and camaraderie. Later in the evening, I find a seat between Jarkko and Juliette, and discreetly tell them about my last few days at work, especially about Professor Norris, and Mrs Bransen-Bowes.

They find it all fascinating, but are neither surprised nor shocked. Jarkko reckons that the professor is probably feeling the noose of academic censorship loosening as he contemplates his own death, but does not care to comment on whether he thinks the professor is actually right about humanoid history. Juliette is altogether more lucid, and as someone who works for the Scottish government, she meets people like Mrs Bransen-Bowes on a regular basis, self-indulgent, conceited, arrogant, egotistical bullies, with a touch of the sociopath about them, layering on the 'caringness' whilst being utterly self-centred and brutally selfish.

Jarkko wonders if he can get a shot of driving a hearse, whilst Juliette thinks that crematoriums should have open days for public visits. Someone else interrupts us to ask if I have ever layed down in a coffin to see if it is comfortable. I explain that the more expensive caskets have mattresses and cushions, and more elbow room, and that this is reflected in the costs of these styles of coffins. The questioner seems reassured with my answer, and then we change the subject back to whisky, and if anyone has tried the new Laphroaig Cairdeas 12yo cask strength.

It's supposed to be very good.

Jarkko states that recent bottlings from Cadenhead of Caol Ila have been amazing. Apparently, they do some very good rums too, and cognacs. I make a mental note to visit Edinburgh soon, or even better

Campbeltown, as the shop is bigger there. You learn a lot at whisky club. Whisky really helps the conversation to flow.

I love it.

Chapter Nine - An expensive bottle of whisky & a vicious murder & a brand ambassador pontificates & afternoon tea with seafarer Tom.

There are a lot of curious faces as I enter the main office of Co-operative Funeralcare in Shieldhall. It has been a few years now since we left the cavernous and atmospheric space of Scotland Street garage and decanted all the vehicles down to the modern prefabricated units at Shieldhall, just across from the sewage treatment plant and along from the Southern General Hospital.

We all have to settle in quickly, however, Scotland Street is missed. It had atmosphere and character. Shieldhall does not.

Curious faces give me their undivided attention as I enter the room. A cardboard box containing a bottle of whisky has just been delivered by the postman. This has aroused a lot of curiosity in the premises as several such parcels have already been delivered within the last couple of months.

Eddie Allen, the transport manager shuffles across from his small office at the front door in a pair of house slippers, looking like an affable grandad from a vintage comic book. He is a warm-hearted man, and less bossy than his predecessor Manny 'the maltese budgie'. Eddie seems to quite enjoy taking delivery of small boxes at reception from a bewildered postman who is wondering why the undertakers are needing all this fancy single malt whisky these days.

Andy Barr and Boaby Gray are standing at the front door skiving, smoking, and clocking everything that's happening.

In the office sits Mags, the funeral assistant, a stern business-like and rather small woman with a penchant for sentiment and cigarettes. Her tight short curly hair gives her a masculine look, and Andy Barr calls her 'Mabozza' as, in his opinion, she has bigger balls than her husband. Generally people in Shieldhall agree with him.

Margaret ignores the recently landed box of whisky and continues to process a pile of funeral arrangements laying across her desk in a manner of mild irritation.

Opposite her sits Gordano Furioso, not his real name, his real name is Gordon Forrester, but due to his likeable volatility and keenness for hard liquor, along with a wicked sense of humour, and the fact that he likes to think of himself as a sort-of Italian gangster, we all call him Gordano Furioso. Today he is furiously demanding to see what's in the box recently delivered by the postman, supposedly containing single malt whisky.

I am handed a pair of scissors by Eddie Allen, who likes a drop or two of Glenmorangie 10yo at Christmas, so is something of a whisky expert, and I break the taped seal around the box. Inside is a green sturdy cardboard box with a small brass-looking clasp, and therein is a bottle of Macallan 12 year old Woodland Sherry Oak.

"So when you goin' to open it ralfy?" demands Gordano, easing his ample but agile frame around from his desk to get a closer look.

"Not now and not ever, this is a banker!" I state.

"Whaaat!" exclaims Eddie, "But whisky is supposed to be drunk".

Gordano chimes in, "So do we get a splash to see if it's any good, or is it that fancy pish that you keep bumpin' on about at that stupid whisky club of yours?"

I keep my dignity, whilst suppressing the laughter inside. This is very entertaining.

I point calmly towards the box of whisky now sitting on a desk for all to see. "That bottle," I state, "Has cost me one hundred pounds!"

There is an audible gasp from around the room.

"Wait a minute, how much did you say there?" demands Andy Barr.

"One hundred pounds." I confirm.

"Whaat the fuck," exclaims Boaby Gray, "I can have a month of nights out at the Station Bar for that money, wee fowlers, ready salted crisps and dark rums, all night long."

"You must be off your head you stupid arsehole!" declares Andy Barr un-humorously.

Mags stares intensely up from her processing jobs, "Well a fool and his money!" she sighs.

Gordano has a glint of mischief in his eyes, "So if you open that bottle right now, we can all have an expensive malt, then you top it up again and seal it so no one knows when they're daft enough to buy it at auction."

"The bottle remains sealed, anyway with all your immature, unseasoned palettes, you lot would never appreciate its finer nuances and subtleties." I proclaim breezily.

There is a mutter of contemptuous expletives around the room . . . which is quite entertaining.

"Why have you spent so much money on a young whisky ralfy,"asks Eddie.

"Because part of my undertakers stash is for selling in a few years at auction, where I will make about four times my money."

"Never in a million years," spits Boaby, ". . . will people be stupid enough to pay good money for that, when there's plenty to go round, and always will be."

"Well, I think I know better than you lot, and I predict that I will get up to four hundred pounds for this in about ten years' time, so it's a good punt, a good investment, four times my money over ten years, and better than the stock market."

"Well you're just an idiot, and it will never happen." concludes Andy Barr, and heads off to the front door for another cigarette.

He's smoking roll-ups these days as ordinary cigarettes are now £5.00 a packet of 20, twice what they were five years before, which was when I finally stopped smoking. A pack of rolling tobacco, about 50 grams, will set you back £4.50 and provide, if modestly rolled, around 30 cigarettes. So there is a saving to be had. I laugh to myself at their indignation at the cost of my Macallan Woodland bottling. They pay over two thousand pounds a year on their smoking habit, and even in 2006, most of my colleagues at Shieldhall are still smoking around 20 a day, oblivious to the health consequences.

I place the whisky, wrapped safely inside its delivery box, into the back of my car, so as to get it home to the stash as soon as possible to join my other growing assortment of collectable bottlings. Highland Park 30yo, Brora 21yo, Port Ellen 25yo, Millburn 18yo, and other rarities, which are all now part of my pension plan, after all I do hate saving in banks.

I just don't trust them.

A lot has changed recently. The old management have been paid off, a sort of early retirement, before they were either ready or prepared. Mr Dick has lost his job, in a reorganisation initiative, and he simply disappears from sight, and then from memory, like he never existed. He is not missed. His influence is over.

Pencils are delighted now that they have more chance of survival now he's gone! He sure had a lot of power over his employees when he had his job, but now he has none, just a very generous pension, and probably, nothing to do with himself but sit and wait.

John Farrell reluctantly goes, as do his colleagues, and they are replaced with a new generation of managers, who like the last ones, and due to lack of proper leadership within the Co-operative movement, just get on with doing enough to get by.

I'm a senior funeral director now, fully qualified with a National Association of Funeral Directors diploma, and also, a diploma from the British Institute of Embalmers, undeniably, the most interesting course I have ever taken, and with the best pass marks I have ever achieved in exams.

It's interesting, different, practical and needed in the modern funeral environment.

Unlike the old days, by which I mean, recent old days, families no longer feel the need to arrange funerals within two to three days. A week or more is the new normal. Some funerals are being arranged several weeks away now as families wait for distant relatives to arrive from different parts of the world, or choose to have the scheduled holiday first, before the funeral takes place.

Alec the van driver has retired, old Hughie the hearse driver has retired, and many familiar faces simply fade suddenly from view to occasionally be seen at shops, resorts, or intimated as a funeral notice in a local paper, or perhaps mentioned in gossip in the staffroom. I can really feel time rolling by now, and it feels strange, a speeding-up cycle of funerals, arrangements, whisky club, whisky festivals and sitting in coffee shops in Byres road. Sometimes I go out on my motorbike, usually heading south, ending up at Bladnoch again to visit Raymond Armstrong, and to see how the distillery is getting on. Raymond shows me around his warehouses, and I love it.

The whisky scene provides a growing sense of community, which is now in contrast to the co-operative, what with all the organising, then re-organising, then consultants, then 'initiatives', then promises quickly abandoned, then more change for changes sake, and a growing army of unproductive managers sitting around in the new head office at Balloon Street, Manchester.

Then funeral prices go up, get more expensive, and administrators get greedier.

Those of us who have experience, and who know the Co-op, can smell the high-level incompetence and consequential decay from what the Co-op once was, a mutual business that successfully served communities.

No longer though, it is a mutual business which serves itself, specifically, senior management.

I know the smell of decay. The Co-op is decaying. It shows more and more in the quality of service provision, and in the frustration of ground-level managers who are not allowed to manage due to the intensity of bureaucracy. Being fully qualified as a funeral director, I am asked if I would like to be a manager.

I bluntly decline.

It's a no-brainer.

A mugs move.

I will stick to being a foot soldier, they are always needed. Managers are easy replaced at the whim of the establishment. I watch managers arrive and then leave, their ambitions for betterment turned to dust. It's real life. I will stick to doing the *real* job. I am less dispensable.

───────────────────────────

I'm off desk duties and out on the van today. Since Alec retired, and headed off to sit in his conservatory, built specifically for his retirement, I will be out with either Dolly or Hugh. Dolly is a little man, conservative and rather pedestrian, completely dedicated to doing his portion of the work only, and disregarding everything else that is going on. It's his way of coping with the ritual of his employment. It is a daily habit and Dolly loves his habits. He has the habit of eating the same type of home-made sandwich every single day, and before he eats it, will lift the corner of the bread just to see what's in the filling. He always knows what's in the filling, he made the damn thing himself, he says that he does.

After the sandwich, and a cup of tea, which takes ten minutes exactly to drink, he will head to the toilet for a shit lasting ten minutes, same time, every day, and it bugs me considerably.

Dolly once told me he was a whisky fan, and 'loved a good drop of malt', so I gave him a decent measure from my stash, in a cleaned glass bottle which he gladly accepted, and in return, a few days later, he provided a teaspoons worth of blended scotch in a plastic pop bottle, handing it over like it was the crown jewels. Miserable wee shit! Every day with Dolly is a dull, uneventful day.

Hugh is very different. Moody, thin, ill-looking, pale, dark, sullen, sombre, serious and very mercurial, he looks every inch what a morbid victorian undertaker should look like. Essentially, like an animated corpse radiating modest and measured sympathy to bereaved humans. I call him Jiffy, after a brand of lemon scented scouring chemical cleaner.

It seems appropriate.

Jiffy is now the longest serving senior funeral director, and also the only one without formal qualifications for the job, which, due to his diligence, does not prevent him in any way from doing his jobs properly.

Many of his more qualified colleagues bring less competency to the profession, especially the managers.

Today I'm out on the van with Jiffy. I collect the paperwork and head to where he usually lurks.

When I find him, he is sitting in the changing area, attached to the staff room and separated by some rippled glass and a light wood veneered door which remains open, even when it's closed. It is in fact a handy place to find some peace and quiet, and to be left alone, undisturbed. He is sitting in front of his locker, staring deeply into the abyss before him. Lost in his world of gothic horror.

He is a very interesting man.

I remember the first time I was out on the van with him.

The silence was deafening, until I tried to generate some conversation.

"I hear you're into bikes Hughie!" I suggested, looking to break the ice. Jiffy answered with silence.

"And you were a leader in a biker gang when you used to be a bin man!"

Jiffy turned towards me, face sullen as the grave.

"Are you taking the piss?" he enquired darkly. We continued in silence.

These days, now we know each other better, I find him to be almost cheerful, sometimes, but not very often. He is the classic epitome of what an undertaker is expected to be by society.

I hand him the black, plastic folder of our days work. "Four coffins for branch viewings. Oh, and, errr, a box of copy paper to go to Newcross parlour". Jiffy sighs as he gets to his feet.

He declares to everybody listening, "I hate this place". I believe he does.

Jiffy has no need to lie. He's not the sort.

We head off through the Clyde tunnel which is a dreary, cement-lined conduit road connecting the north to the south of the city under the river. Within a couple of hours we have completed all our tasks, and are about to head back to Shieldhall for some lunch when the van phone rings. "That's an emergency police removal in Drumchapel, and you're the nearest so you will have to do it, soon, and do you have a stretcher in the van?" whines a voice from the control desk. We affirm that we do.

Soon we have arrived in Kilbowie, and drive into Cornock Street, a quiet, sheltered residential cluster of modern low-rise flats.

We don't need to search out the flat number as two police cars are directly outside the front door.

A pale and clearly distressed police woman walks rapidly towards the van, gesturing us to lower the windows so she can talk.

"Do you have protective suits and gloves?" she enquires.

"This is a bad one, really distressing, so just letting you know that you will be shocked."

Jiffy and I are intrigued.

It is not often that undertakers are about to be 'shocked'.

I gather the stretcher from out the back of the van, along with extra gloves, just in case, and we are led into the close which is spotlessly clean, fresh scented and domesticated with pots of geraniums in full bloom. We enter the small door of a ground floor flat and notice immediately the well-cared for attention that an elderly person would give to their home, clean, fresh vacuumed carpet, dusted ceramic ornaments of sentimental posed animals, and all seems ordinary except for the stench of blood in the air.

On entering the front room, we are shocked at the blood sprayed across the walls, even up to the ceiling, and extending into the kitchenette where a pool of congealing blood is turning brown around the sink. Water is still running from the tap.

On the floor, laying still and lifeless and covered in her own blood, lays an elderly woman, probably in her eighties. Jiffy, myself and the police lady stand silently, surveying the scene in front of us. This has been violent, vicious and brutal.

The old woman has had her throat cut, seemingly shallow, several times, then repeatedly stabbed across the chest and neck many times. We all feel the violence in the air, the silence of the shock to the atmosphere.

I feel a sudden surge of anger, real anger.

Who would do such a thing?

I unfold the stretcher and lay it flat beside the corpse. I unfold the white plastic sheet, and lay it carefully over the stretcher. With gloves on, Jiffy and I carefully lift the stiff light body of the old woman onto the stretcher and fold over the plastic to cover the trauma. As we do so, her clothes entirely covered in her own drying blood, a small neatly folded cotton handkerchief falls out of her apron pocket. It is perfectly white, untouched by blood, and on the corner it reads, in hand stitched letters, 'Home Sweet Home'.

It is the following week that I conduct a funeral to Clydebank crematorium. Gordon, the attendant, is keen to tell me some news. Somehow, he seems to know that I attended the removal of the woman from Cornock Street. Whilst the mourners commence their first of two hymns in the chapel, he tells me that the old lady was murdered by her grandson, who stabbed her over thirty times because she had no more money in her purse to give him for drugs.

She had given him all she could, then more, but it was not enough.

He was arrested, charged, went to court, and was convicted of violent assault leading to accidental death.

On the grounds of diminished responsibility, the charge of murder was dropped.

After a short stay in prison, he returned to the community with his new-gained reputation of being a 'tough guy' and demanded money under threat from other residents. He stabbed his mother on two occasions for money, and she refused to press charges.

He stabbed two children outside the newsagents over a bag of sweets.

The families affected were encouraged by police to drop their complaint.

He built his 'reputation' as a tough guy and a 'player'. The following year he died of a heroin overdose. Only his mother attended the funeral. She never shed a tear during the committal, or afterwards.

115

It's whisky club night, Tuesday evening 7pm. I am just finishing a plate of mushroom soup at the Bon Accord, before the troops arrive along with about twenty bottles of whisky. The bottles remain in their boxes tonight as we are in for a delightful surprise. A brand ambassador is going to give us free samples of a distillery official range and talk about the product. We have had a few good brand reps, telling us interesting things about cask management and stuff, so we have growing expectation for the evening ahead.

The brand ambassador arrives, with a small folding barrow supporting a large secure travel container of six assorted bottlings from the big distillery. The brand ambassador is super friendly and personally says hello to all the club members individually, walking round the tables, shaking hands, before he commences his presentation. Glasses are already placed around the tables, on provided paper mats, clearly indicating which specific malt is in the positioned glass so as to avoid confusion.

We do quickly notice however, that the pour levels in the glasses are very low, just enough for a sip, but not much of a taste.

The brand ambassador clinks an empty glass repeatedly for attention then commences his presentation.

We all sit to attention, waiting patiently for our first sip. It takes a while.

The brand ambassador has a lot to say first. "Our water is sourced from the Auchinibooglie River which cascades down Ben Auchinibooglie from a height of 2,500 metres through unblemished natural habitat of indigenous trees and shrubs".

"And sheep shit!" interjects one of the club members quietly, much to everyone's amusement. The brand ambassador is unfazed, and continues without missing a beat.

"And collects in our personal distillery loch just above our visitor centre where we let it settle and purify further before filtering it into the distillery for making our very, very special whisky."

The brand ambassador pauses dramatically, raising his hand as if blessing the audience, "Now, would you like to taste the unique precious liquid?"

There is a nod of affirmation around the tables, and we all raise our first glass for a sip. It is slightly rough, young, nippy, but flavoursome, with very little sign of maturity. "Isn't that just the best young malt you've ever tasted then?" quips the ambassador. "No!" replies a club member quietly from a nearby table.

The Ambassador is totally unfazed and carries on.

"And then we steep the malted barley in the hot water three times to create the sweet and delicious juice for fermenting using our unique yeast which is perfect for a fast and efficient fermentation. And now some fascinating history of the distillery!" at which point, the audience sits for over twenty minutes listening to tales of distillery mousing cats, ghosts in the grain store, and the manager who hung himself in warehouse 13 in 1933 after his wife ran off with a sailor.

By the time we get to try the second whisky, two club members are falling asleep. One has started to snore quietly.

"And after passing through our copper pot stills, the whisky emerges at last released by the still from the captivity of fermented wash, which is very tasty if you have a cold and need extra vitamins . . . ha ha ha."

The third whisky is not very pleasant. It is dark coloured, flat tasting and featureless, lacking character and strength. "And specially created by our superstar master blender, Hughie McHugh M.B.E., who we just call Hugh, and he's quite famous with the connoisseurs in Germany. We have our exclusive travel retail single malt called the 'Beastie of Auchinibooglie' a treble matured PX sherry and Oloroso sherry-finished malt with time spent in warehouse 13 where the angels feast on their share and bless us as guardians of our heritage and history". He continues, "And is exclusively available only at airports, so you better book a flight somewhere now . . . ha, ha."

A silence descends onto Glasgow's whisky club, as the malts start to turn a little sour in the glass. I can't help it, I have to ask a question to break the monotony of the evening.

"There looks like caramel colourant in this, and chill filtration too?"

The brand ambassador gives me a passing glare, and dives into my question. "And the natural colour is *enhanced* naturally with the small addition of caramel, but, you won't taste that. And yes, we do chill filter because our customers like their whisky to be pure and free of impurities".

"You know!" he adds with a frown, "Our customers complain if their whisky becomes all cloudy and hazy when they add ice, and, it just ruins the expectations of purity that they expect from us. I can personally assure you," he adds looking sincere, and slightly irritated now, "That the addition of natural colour and chill filtration do not affect or change the excellence of the product in any way whatsoever."

"How about the fact that this is a basic strength of 40% alcohol, does that not change the excellence of the product?" asks a fed-up club member. "No, not at all, 40% is the perfect strength for delivering the uniqueness of the brand to the consumer, any stronger would make it unpalatable, and our master blender insists that all whisky should be bottled at 40% for palatability," retorts the ambassador. We taste the third, fourth, fifth and sixth drams, all as dull as the commentary. Even the 'aged' 18yo version is a caramel-loaded bitter cask concoction which the brand ambassador describes as 'a barman's dream, boasting its age discreetly, but not ashamed to feature in high-end cocktails and boutique beverages.'

A soft sigh ripples round the room, and sensing the change in atmosphere a club official quickly steps in to offer a big 'thank you' on behalf of the club to the brand ambassador for his presentation and samples. The contents of the glasses are instantly abandoned as club members wander off to buy a pint at the bar and source clean glasses for a dram or four, or more, from existing club stocks, sitting in a large cardboard box by the kitchen door. The brand ambassador seems relieved that his night is over, and goes round the club handing out Auchinibooglie gift pens along with a voucher offering £5 off any product bought at the distillery shop after an official tour. He then leaves to go somewhere else.

Club members quickly help tidy up the tables, removing glasses for washing and emptying discarded whisky into a galvanised metal bucket, which fills up rapidly. We never hear from the distillery again, although their new non-age statement port wood triple matured 'Amazing Grace' bottling wins a global whisky award at some international competition somewhere and gets absolutely rave reviews from all the carefully selected experts who receive generous hospitality and free bottles at the official launch at Edinburgh Castle on midsummer's night. Apparently, bar professionals and mixologists just love its 'versatility'. Customers who buy the bottles at airport shops are indifferent.

One independent drinks commentator describes it as 'woody juice and sugar syrup with whisky in the distance'. They receive an e-mail from a distillery nominated boutique consultant advising them that they are 'misunderstanding' the brand, and offering three free bottles as a 'gift'.

It is amazing how much you learn and how quickly you learn at an active whisky club, especially when so near to the scotch whisky Industry as Glasgow's whisky club is. In the space of five years my knowledge of whisky grows enormously, and I learn less from the 'brand ambassadors' than I do just chatting to the ordinary people who work in, and around the Industry. Generally, they are fine people, just getting on with their jobs, and life. I love it all, but will stick to being an undertaker, as this job keeps me keen on whisky, whereas, if I worked in the Industry, I know I would soon get jaded and demotivated by the real environment and challenges of it all. At the end of the day, it's just sales, sales, sales. At least the small independent distilleries do it with some style, character and grace. I have never ever visited a large automated distillery operation that never left me feeling slightly empty and cold after the experience.

There's an arrangement just come into the office at Shieldhall, and I am the only one available with experience, so the job is mine. A pre-arrangement, a not-yet-dead arrangement, a plan-before-you-die arrangement, and I am just in the mood for this type of arrangement, because it is always a better atmosphere in a house when you arrange for someone who is actually still alive. The address is unusual, number 16 Robertson Street, in the city centre and down by the river Clyde and not a known residential street, more of an office and 'administrative hub' sort of street.

I leave the work car at the carpark in Paisley Road, and walk across the new 'Squiggly' bridge over the Clyde and just to my right is the beginning of Robertson Street. The building is grand, and imposing, and I have been here a few years ago as part of 'Glasgows Open Doors Day' initiative where members of the public can see around buildings and premises not normally open to the public.

The building is the Clydeport Authorities Office, very grand with its Victorian-era opulence, grace and beauty, especially the magnificent stone carvings both outside and inside, and opulent marble staircase.

I press the doorbell for access around the side of the building and am immediately buzzed in via the intercom. Two floors up via an old fashioned gated elevator is a small, neat office with pictures of ships and boats from around the world, and this is where I meet Tom the sailor. A very weathered, kindly-looking and soft spoken elderly man, he looks wiry and fit for his age, and evidently has a clear head and an intelligent disposition. Tom wishes to pre-arrange his funeral, but quickly stresses that he is not looking to actually buy a plan and he hopes he is not wasting my day. "That's not a problem Tom," I say, "You got me out of the boring old office for the afternoon, so just take your time and we can put together an individual plan for you that you can use anywhere."

I open my folder and prepare a fresh arrangement sheet, along with a list of considerations and advice for those recently bereaved, or about to be.

Tom puts on a kettle over by the window, and offers me a cup of tea, standard 'British' tea as there is no other option, which is fine.

As the fresh-brews arrive, made with loose tea and not the usual teabags, I settle back to listen to the old man, and hear a little of his story.

"I'm a part time lecturer along at the Nautical College in Crown Street, been doing that now for about two years, teaching the practical stuff, simple seamanship skills and such," he pauses, looking into the middle distance for a few seconds.

"Now it seems like I have time to look over my life." he continues.

"Seems like yesterday now when I ran away from home and got a job as a deck hand on an old freighter . . . she was called the 'Imperial Star' and that ship saved my life!"

Tom sips his tea as he tells of his early years. "I was one of fourteen children, the seventh, born 1921 in Govan Road, with the sound of ship building the first thing I ever heard. Things never got better than basic, and as my ma was soon left on her own, her kids had no choice, we had to make our own way in the world as soon as possible, and I was too young to get a job in the ship yards, so one day I boarded a boat in Yorkhill and offered to work for free in exchange for food and a bunk. The captain of the Imperial Star had seen it all before, and took a chance on me. Well . . . I never looked back, and the river took me out into the world beyond and all its challenges." He pauses, deep in his memories. "That was 1934 . . . 65 years ago now."

Tom goes silent, drifting off into his thoughts. I sip my tea, it is lovely, being proper tea leaves, and strong brewed with no sugar added, just a dash of milk. "A wee scrawny boy from Govan, who couldn't even read or write, and I get to see every port in the world, the most violent storms at the Cape, the most brilliant sunsets over the Caribbean, from Shanghai to Sri Lanka, from New Zealand to Newfoundland, from Madagascar to Monaco, I have got to meet so many people at so many places".

Tom sighs, "And here I am, back home to roost where I started". I hear the emotion in his voice, and we both pause to allow the old sailor to recover himself as the nostalgia and memories of an eventful life now flood

121

the office with their presence. As Tom has been speaking, I have been noting down some details whilst listening to his story.

I am offered a top up of tea, which I readily accept, and we chat, passing a couple of hours in the day, as I listen to some more of his tales and travels, and there's plenty to hear.

Pirate attacks in the Gulf of Aden, getting frozen to a railing in Anchorage and almost dying of hypothermia, chilling out with Rastas in Jamaica, finding love in Rio, losing love in Aruba.

Tom is a fascinating man, and modest in his manner, a gent.

I complete a plan for his funeral, which could be tomorrow, or could be in ten years' time, or whenever. Tom is happy with the layout and structure, a simple cremation with college volunteers scattering his ashes from St Andrews suspension bridge at Glasgow Green, into the Clyde. He has a small flat at the Bridgegate where he makes model boats and helps out with the local seaman's union, so knows the area well, and regularly walks around the Green, and along the river.

I leave Tom with his plan and we briefly shake hands as I leave.

Heading out into the rain and traffic, my day has been unexpectedly enriched by meeting this man. Back at the office, it's finishing time, so I head home to my house, my dinner, a roaring fireside, a dram, or perhaps not, perhaps a large tot of rich and warming navy rum.

I pause to offer a heart-felt toast to the shadow of Tom, still lingering close by me in the embers of the day, and with the daylight fading under the eye of a glowing sun setting majestically over the western hills of the Clyde, surrendering the day in a blaze of brilliant orange light, I am soon possessed by the creeping shadows of oncoming night.

Chapter Ten - Distillery open-days & Duties in the Temple of Sobek

I have noticed of late that the dynamics of Glasgow's whisky club are changing, at first slightly, but latterly, more pronounced. Don't get me wrong, it still retains its original welcoming warmth, however as the club grows in membership, there are different groups growing within the club nights at the Bon Accord, which is causing some segregation. This is perfectly natural, and only to be expected, however, the nature of the group is less cohesive and affable than of previous years.

It is decided that a Club day out, with a solid whisky mission will be a good opportunity to bring club members more together, and as Auchentoshan distillery have just announced their first ever family open day, we grab our tickets and hope the weather will be fine and sunny on the big day.

We are not disappointed. One summer Saturday, with the air fresh and slightly breezy, we arrive via public transport to the front gates of this imposing, well-spread out distillery looking resplendent with its fresh whitewashed walls, tar-black roofs and recently manicured lawns and shrubberies.

Staff are most welcoming, and even though I have forgotten to bring my ticket, a quick nod from the supervisor on duty lets me in.

"I love your new YouTube channel, I'm one of your subscribers now," states the supervisor. I'm flattered.

I don't think of my whisky channel as anything particularly special, but am pleased to see it growing steadily, especially after a recent brutal criticism from a more established blog, a sour slap-down, but the best advertising I could ever have hoped for.

It's a good day, and plenty of distractions have been organised by the distillery, with highlights being the masterclasses and opportunity to buy an older bottling of their single malt, straight from the cask, sediment 'bits' and all, and on tasting, a splendid version of Auchentoshans signature light, lowland style.

It is such a good day out, that when Arran distillery arrange their own inaugural open day later in the year, most club members sign up for the visit across the water from Ardrossan to Brodick on the cal-mac ferry to experience this island distillery's hospitality.

A lot of whisky is consumed by club members, many of whom get increasingly vocal, raucous and passively aggressive due to too much consumption of the excellent liquor. On the returning ferry, the more-sober of us start to distance ourselves from the unsociable, and disruptive behaviour of our club companions. On the train up to Glasgow a few of us, mainly older club members sit in a carriage well clear of the rabble rousers that our less discerning whisky-aficionados have become. At the next club meeting the following week, the session appears normal and as would be expected, but something small and subtle has changed. The club has changed.

After a few drinks, and an hour or so into our club night, the wee comments start about my growing YouTube review channel. "A flash in the pan!" declares a club official, somewhat sneeringly.

My friend Juliette leaps to my defence, "Just ignore him," she says affirmatively.

I do.

"So will you be sharing all the free bottles you're getting with us?" asks someone who has recently joined the group.

"All you do is ask for bottles in exchange for good reviews, which is what all the experts do all the time, and then you can charge advertising for good reviews that get attention . . . then you get hospitality and exclusive bottlings and such!"

I smile and ignore the loaded comment from the person, who happens to be a journalist.

He continues, "It may be a nice little earner for you so long as you don't criticize too much and speak your mind, oh! And do try to make your presentation a bit more slick, just watch how the BBC does it, or SingleMalt TV . . . they're really good". I listen to the well-intentioned advice, then disregard it. I will do what works for me.

Later that evening, back at home, and still remarkably sober considering how much whisky I could have drunk, but didn't, I reach into the undertakers stash and pull out a bottle of Laphroaig, a recent release at cask strength, Feis Ile 2008, bought from a friend who was on Islay for the festival the previous year and bought six bottles. It is lovely stuff, and I refill my glencairn glass a few times before the sleepiness of peated intoxication by a glowing fireside forces me into the carpet, where I begin to doze off. Soon, I hear a cat purring near to me, which means Orlando is present, and I will soon be somewhere else. It's just what happens in these moments.

The air is cool and moving slowly across the River Nile with a gentleness which ripples the loosened sails of moored feluccas, resting now after a day's trading up or down the banks of this great river, meandering as it does through the Sahara sand, barren and golden in its presence. The smell of myrrh and another exotic resin wafts down to the river's edge from the temple above which I recognise immediately. I have returned to the temple of Sobek at Kom Ombo.

I wander up with some intrepidation as to whether Anubis has summoned me again. He has, and as I enter the great hall of the crocodile god, I see Anubis standing by the altar, assisted by two companions, one of whom is Thoth, god of the moon, and the other, by her feline features, is Bastet, the goddess of protection.

The temple is otherwise empty of worshipers, and all that is noticeably present are seven large books laid out, open, on stone plinths along the south wall.

I then notice Sobek, standing at the array of books, a page-turning wand in his hand, musing the wisdom there-in as he turns the pages slowly, and with great ceremony. Sobek beckons me over to him, and introduces the books, one by one.

All are books of the dead.

The Tibetan book, the Egyptian book, the Chinese book, the Mexican book, the North book, the Namibian book, and lastly, the magnificent Agarthian book. All are opened at the same page, and as Sobek turns the pages with his wand, all pages turn together as one.

"Light, life and love to the gods of Egypt," I say aloud.

"Thank you." replies Sobek.

Anubis leaves his fellow gods at the altar, and come across to speak to me.

"Are you doing well?" asks Anubis.

"Yes, just fine," I reply.

The god stares at me with intensity, "Good!"

"You are honourable in your service to the dead, and to the living, so I will let you look into the books of the dead, which read complete when read together."

I move forwards to more clearly see the words in the books, and as I do so they all merge into one under the spells of Sobek.

I see the great cycles.

The harmony of the eternal spheres.

The enormity of it all.

The duality of light and dark.

The reconciliation in the presence of the divine goddess.

I hear the weavers loom spinning out the dimensions of spaces and times.

I hear the passage of many feet, hushed and muted, moving across the great divide.

I reach out and briefly touch eternity.

I am undone, and made whole again.

I embrace the Lord Anubis.

I am reassured.

I walk out from the temple, and down stone steps onto the shifting desert sands leading towards the banks of the river. A boat is moored, a small dhow, full-sailed and set to leave. An orange cat lies comfortably astern, passively watchful and waiting. I loosen the moorings and we drift gently off into the middle of the river where it is swiftest, and with the soft breeze filling the sail, we glide gently through the star-lit night and into the dawning of a fresh, new day.

Chapter Eleven - Davy D & Ginger Gray & a trip to a bothy.

I cannot believe just how many years it is now that I have been working as an undertaker. How time flies, but as an undertaker for eighteen years, I know the real value of time. Time is the one resource that is worth more than money, but only when it's realised that we need it most and then we find that money cannot buy it. That is, of course, unless one plans ahead, creating financial resources through negating personal debt and in having enough cash to allow an early retirement, a few extra years, of quitting the rat race, of terminating the repetitive work-routine, the hopeless traffic commute that is the reality of too many people in today's hectic world.

Time is never properly valued by humanoids, even when it is too late to recover time.

I have been thinking about this again, sitting as I am in a hearse on a wet, cold, Monday night being driven back from a chapel in the east-end at 8.30pm, feeling cold, tired and deflated. My driver tonight is Davy Doolally. Davy looks like a Shakespearean simpleton or, a dizzy half-wit from a medieval comedy play. 'Doolally' is not his real name, but we call Davy, 'Davy-Doolally' as he is slow, over-methodical, irritatingly habitual, and drinks coffee from a mug in a most unusual manner, clasping his thumb under the handle rather than over it, a most uncomfortable thing to do, but this never bothers Davy-Doolally.

He also has a habit of braking and slowing the hearse going through green traffic lights, whilst accelerating towards red traffic lights, braking violently to a halt . . . not dignified. He is a weak and tediously mild man to the point of anodyne, and he irritates the hell out of me. When in his presence on a job, I will usually end up taking the piss out of him, suggesting that his wife, Jean, who is big and bossy, will pump him up the arse when he gets home, because she has the balls and he is her bitch. Davy does not find this amusing, which makes such comments all the funnier when there's plenty of people around enjoying the wind-ups' and banter, which, of course is always funnier than tame banter.

The hearse is the last of the Daimler Benz models, very expensive, and very fuel-inefficient. Considering that the engine is a four and a half litre monster, you would think that there would be some decent heating in the front seats, but no, there's not. The hearse looks great, very 'stately' with wonderful road presence, and it grips the tarmac like a limpet. Even when flying along the motorway at 70mph, the vehicle still looks calm, cool, dignified and slow. It's not slow, it's a flying machine, and speed has saved us on numerous occasions where we have been running late between jobs, either held up by long-winded clergy, or from engagements scheduled to close together. These things happen.

Tonight, we're just going slow, proper slow, due to slow commuter traffic along the main roads, and also, Davy-Doolally is driving, which means it will take us an extra fifteen minutes to get back to the garage. I sink back into the solid leather seat, crouching down so I'm slightly below the window sill on the door, and start to doze off. It's already been a long and busy day. I'm tired.

I'm steadily falling asleep, despite Davy trying to keep me awake with his boring family talk about this, that, and whatever, in fact, the monotone mumble from Davy is helping me nod-off. As the sound of motorway traffic, rain and mumbles recedes, I find myself laying on a blanket of warm, dry sand, on a small undulating sand-dune somewhere in the north of Scotland. Behind me lays a small, sturdy, stone-built bothy, huddled safely into the turf, with a yellow-painted window frame and a gloss painted green door. Inside, a bright fire burns within the grate, warming the humble, but comfortable room and a small oak table by the window keeps my bottles of single malt whiskies safe and ready for the night ahead. The distance periodic whoosh of ocean waves upon fine golden sand repeats in my ears along with the wail of high flying gulls and other sea birds.

It is bliss, I am alone, and I am in paradise. My days belong to me, my time is my own, and I can lay in silence listening to the planet breathe around me, expressing its wonder within the landscape and in the fall of sun light across the horizons. The sun is glorious, the sun is beautiful, the sun is life to my reality.

The hearse door slams shut.

We are back in the garage.

I make my way, still half asleep to my car, scraping off the accumulating ice which has formed in the cold night damp, and I drive home to bed, sleep, and hopefully, some more of my wonderful dream.

Jiffy is in the changing rooms adjacent to the communal staff room, and he is staring into the abyss again. Cold, dark, and silent, Jiffy contemplates the pain of life, and the stupidity of people, and continues to stare into the abyss in front of him.

I am getting to quite like the guy. He is a biker, and rides a Suzuki, whilst I, having just bought a motorbike, am riding a Triumph T-bird Sport. It is heavy, torque-y, solid and fast. I am going on weekend day-trips to Lindesfarne, Loch Lomond, St Andrews and to Bladnoch. There's a distillery at Bladnoch where I am always made welcome. I like the place.

Jiffy does not like the Co-op at Shieldhall. He hates the place, and frequently says so, but still gets on and does his job anyway. He seems to like the actual job, it suits him, and he looks like an undertaker out of a 'Carry On' film. He likes the 'Carry On' films. He is an avid fan. We are on the van today, and it's getting quieter as the winter death-rate falls with the arrival of spring, and the natural world gives old people a reason to live a little longer with longer, warmer days.

There are two coffins to be delivered to parlours on the south side for viewing in the afternoon, and as the embalmers have not yet finished preparing them, there is no hurry to leave the hub, so we have another cup of tea. We talk 'bikes' for a bit, then he talks bikes whilst I talk whisky.

As soon as we have dropped off and set up the second coffin for viewing at the parlour at Queen Street, Rutherglen, the van phone rings, all the vehicles have fixed phones these days, you can't stop progress. I answer the phone, and note down the details of a nursing home removal just five minutes away at Rutherglen care home. It will not take us long to get there.

When Jiffy and I arrive, we are ushered to a quiet corner of the large, expansive modern low-level facility which is more like a slow-motion hospital than an actual 'care-home'. Having unfolded our folding stretcher, we follow strict Co-op policy and attach a name tag to the deceased, a tiny, frail, old lady who it appears, has been subject to emergency resuscitation judging by the stick-pads and wires still attached to her lifeless body. Her fragile blouse has been ripped open to expose her chest, and the ambulance personnel who attended her as she was dying are responsible. They are, after all, just doing their job. The nurse who is with us to witness the removal suddenly bursts into tears.

Jiffy and I stop what we are doing immediately and allow the distressed lady to calm down a little before I ask her a question. "Sorry," I say, "Is this lady quite close to you, do you wish to leave the room whilst we attend to removing her?" "No, no," sobs the nurse, "Not at all, but I just feel so guilty and I can't speak to anyone about it."

"Can we help?" I ask.

Still sobbing intermittently, she accepts the paper tissue offered by Jiffy, and tells us her story. As a newly qualified care nurse, she had been allocated six patients to look after, and the deceased was one of them. They immediately bonded as the old woman was always appreciative and polite to her helper. It was two months later that the old woman started to go downhill, starting with a viral infection which would simply not clear up despite all the medications prescribed by her doctor. In fact, if anything, the quantity of medications seemed to be making her worse.

Some family visited, but only for short periods as they had jobs and families of their own, and, after all, the care home was now her family. One of her sons however, was making visits more frequently and angrily demanded to know why a ring was missing from his mother's finger. He soon calmed down when the ring was produced from the manager's office, it was slipping off his mother's shrinking finger, and the carers did not want it to get lost. Soon enough, he was complaining about the chocolate biscuits he brought his mother from Marks and Spencers were missing too, but then, again was placated when it was brought to his attention that his mother had swapped the biscuits for plain ones as she did not like chocolate.

One evening he phoned the home and demanded to speak to the manager, where he asked if his mother was being poisoned by negligent staff, and insisting that if his mother fell out of bed, he would be suing.

This, unfortunately, set a tone of anxiety in the care of his mother by her allotted nurse.

As the old woman was slipping quietly away one week-day evening, her carer panicked at the thought of the son's reaction to the forthcoming news, so she called an ambulance to take the old woman to hospital. She could then not be held 'responsible'. When the ambulance arrived, the medics immediately set about keeping the old woman alive, attempting to resuscitate her for over an hour before giving up and leaving. The duty doctor was not happy with the delay caused by the paramedics, and the carer was feeling bad for causing a peaceful death to become a violent experience for the old woman she cared about. The son was phoned, but as he was now away on business, told the nursing home 'just to get on with it'.

I offer a few words of comfort to the nurse, but there is not really much I can say, or that Jiffy chooses to add. It's part of the journey in life, where we do the best we can, but sometimes our best just goes wrong, and we are subject to blame and dismissal. On the way back to Shieldhall I discuss the situation with Jiffy. He says, "You're best to do your own thing, make the best of what you have, and remember that family are people you know that may not be your friends."

I think he's right.

Ginger Gray is dead. He died at home on the eleventh floor of a high-rise flat in Cowcaddens at the ripe old age of sixteen, and has now been brought to Shieldhall in a plastic bag, soliciting awkward stares on the underground train from other passengers. We pick up Boaby and Ginger from Govan

132

underground station, and Boaby insists on carrying Ginger in the bag in the front of the van. The orange tip of Ginger's tail sticks out between the handles of the plastic bag and we don't know whether to offer sympathy or laugh.

Boaby phones Craigton Crematorium as soon as he gets in the office and ask how much a cremation will be, seeing as it's only a cat, which is a lot smaller than a human and will use less heat. The crematorium supervisor refuses to cremate a cat in a human crematorium as it could cause a terrible fuss, especially if it hit the tabloids, and they always lie, no matter what.

Boaby is a bit stumped, until it is suggested that he contact the pet undertakers listed in the phone book. They are called and it does not take him long to establish that they charge £150 for a cremation. Boaby hangs up on them in disgust and complains loudly about the costs of pet funerals, which we reassure him, is in fact good value as a pet is a cherished member of the family, and should have no expense spared. Boaby, being a tight-wad, does not see it that way, and goes out to the front door for a smoke with his pal Andy Barr, and to formulate another plan.

Soon enough, he is ringing up Glasgow University to see if he can donate Ginger for scientific anatomical research. They politely decline his offer. He is not amused at their indifference. "They could have let they medical students for animals, you know, . . . vets, . . . get experience with Ginger, or even stuff him and put him in a case for the posh museum up there, but . . . no, not interested, the ungrateful bastards, and there's me giving them Ginger for . . . *free*, not even charging them, and with them having all that money too, they could have at least offered a small payment for my inconvenience."

Nobody in Shieldhall says anything, retaining the atmosphere of serenity, sympathy and concern for his bereavement . . . some scurry through to the coffin factory next door to pish themselves laughing without being heard by Boaby and thereby hurting his feelings. He won't hear them laughing there due to all the banging and crashing of coffin assembly. The coffin factory is always a noisy place. Boaby has another cup of tea, before advising the duty manager Graeme that he needs time off duties to dispose of Ginger in a dignified manner.

Graeme advises Boaby that the local Chinese take-away may offer him a fiver for Ginger, where he can then feature in a lunch-time special, complete with boiled rice, bamboo shoots and, of course, fresh ginger! Boaby is not amused.

Andy Barr makes it clear to Boaby that the Co-op undertakers in Shieldhall is the wrong place for dead animals and that he should have wrapped it up in a bin bag and put it in an outside bin. Boaby is not amused.

Big Gordano offers sympathy and suggestions whilst all the while laughing himself silly and using the opportunity to do as little work as possible. Boaby is not amused.

I suggest he phone a local veterinary practice to get professional advice, which he does, then discovers the charge made by a vet to dispose of a small domestic pet animal. Boaby is not amused.

By mid-morning he is beginning to get alarmed at the lack of resources available, free of charge, for the disposal of Ginger. Someone suggests Boaby make a wee cardboard boat for Ginger so that he can sail down the Clyde River on the ebbing current like a Viking funeral, however, Boaby is quick to advise that Ginger hated water, and never took a bath, and he wouldn't want him to drown, even though he's already dead.

It's nearly lunch time when a call comes in from Craigton Crematorium for Boaby, that a sympathetic local vet has an allotment in Inchinnin, at a lovely, quiet spot next to Glasgow International Airport.

Boaby is offered a free internment for his cat at the allotment which is in the process of becoming a Pet Cemetery. Two days later Boaby drives off with Ginger down to Inchinnan and says final farewells to his faithful companion.

At Shieldhall, doors and windows are opened around the staff room as the smell over the last day from Boaby's locker has been a bit 'ripe' with an odour every undertaker recognises.

Ozeum spray and furniture polish are both utilised to help alleviate the stench. When Boaby returns we ask him how it went. "Fine!" he says, "But the bastards asked for a donation for the upkeep of the allotment, and I had to give them a fiver, miserable bastards, imagine, offering a free service and then charging a donation."

"Just terrible Boaby." we respond, heading off to the coffin factory for a laugh.

All is well at Glasgow's whisky club, although at a recent night, I get trapped around a table by two new members, both nursing large, double-pour glasses of better malts which is rather greedy, and wanting my thoughts on what whiskies are now 'investable'. I'm in a good mood, but wary of their mock-friendliness and faux familiarity.

"Macallan, Springbank, anything from closed distilleries." I respond cheerily.

"How about that Bruichladdich?" they ask, paying very close attention to my reply.

I'm feeling a bit cold about this now.

"Black arts, yellow submarine, anything 'local grain'," I respond.

They have their answer now, and leave me sitting beside them, blocked out and no longer included in their conversation. I make a note to avoid them as I have had this recently before, at an Edinburgh whisky fringe festival where two red-faced twits from Bearsden in golfing outfits grilled me at the Glenfarclas table about how 'collectible' Glengoyne was becoming. They were both trying far too hard to be nice and amicable, and the conversation gave me with the shivers. There seems to be more of these types around these days.

Julliette, my most companionable club pal, saunters over with a small pour of Clynelish 14yo. "It's as good as it ever has been, what with that lovely waxiness," she declares. I pour a dram from the emptying bottle sitting amongst the others on the club barrel. After a drop of water and a few sips, I concur with her, it's excellent. A 'character' dram, like Macallan,

Mortlach, Glenfarclas, Springbank, Edradour, Caol Ila, and older bottlings of Talisker, now found at local auction houses.

I have been visiting a local auction house at Finnieston recently, which has started to specialise in bottles of spirits. I rarely bid on the items as there are a few heavy-duty collectors who seem to be bidding furiously on anything of 'quality' that does not look like it has been tampered with, or, maybe it has! I spot a bottle of 1930's Glenlivet with a bare exposed cork, which looks like a hypodermic has been pushed down through the cork. The bottle has a very low fill level for something allegedly 'sealed' and I find myself thinking that it looks faked. This does not stop the bidders though, with the bottle selling for hundreds of pounds.

Buyer beware, buyer take care.

Eventually, I bid on a few unglamorous bottles myself, nothing special or prestigious, just the old unwanted basic brands from the seventies and eighties, pure malts, blended malts, ceramic flasks of old quality blends, and quite a few old versions of White Horse and Teachers. I discuss my purchases at the whisky club, but few are interested choosing instead to chat about what Bruichladdich are going to do next, and why new bottlings of Bowmore are such rubbish quality.

One night, I take an old bottle of Johnnie Walker Green Label 'Pure Malt' to the club, and pour drams for the enthusiasts blind. They are blown away by the quality. Over the next decade, I will watch the quality of Scotch blended whisky disappear into a fake tanned concoction of grain liquor chemicalised soup. Many high profile malts will go the same way, sanitised with chill filtration and infected with E150a chemically burnt sugar.

The Industry only has itself to blame.

Things are changing, the world is changing.

It was an old friend's idea to go for a whisky weekend into the highlands. To stay overnight in one of the bothies again, like we used to before life got in the way. Outside of midgie season of course, for our own comfort.

We are experienced bothy-baggers. I love the bothies. We will just pack up our mountain bikes with alcohol, some food, small cooker, . . . including two bottles of whisky. It's a plan.

I have known Bret for around thirty years now. We met at an Operation Raleigh event in 1983. He is affable, consistent, easy going and spends practically every one of his waking hours outdoors. His home is basic, with only what he needs, which he shares with his girlfriend whom he never intends to marry. She is happy to have it that way, it suits her too as most of her time is spent in voluntary work, mainly nature and the environment, and marital home-bound bliss was never her plans.

With his easy nature, likeability, and average expectations of both himself and others, we tend to get along.

Oh! . . . and we both like single malt whisky.

"We stayed at Cadderlie the last time Bret, how about going there again seeing as we know what it's like?" Bret mulls over my proposal then rejects it quickly. "Na! Still too busy in September and others will have the same idea because it's 'reachable'!"

I move onto another option as I still have, fresh in my mind, the experience of trying to reach a borders bothy a few years back, and finding a stag event of drunken arseholes had monopolised it, forcing us to camp up in the woods, well away from the mayhem below us. It was noisy, and yes, windows were smashed, and several fights broke out. That is the problem with free, accessible accommodation, the arseholes eventually find it.

"How abouts Doune Byre, it's got a nice charm to it!"

Bret mulls over the second option, then decides, "We need to find somewhere less accessible so as if there are others arrive to stay the night, they will probably be civil, and we can give them a dram to shut them up."

"Where then Bret? You decide, Bret's choice!" He ponders a while, looking over a map of Scotland, then points to the north west.

"Kearvaig." he says. "That's well out the way and what with the location, we should get the place to ourselves."

"For fucks sake mate!" I exclaim, "That's six hours drive and the weather up there is completely unpredictable, and getting our bikes over the roughs will be a nightmare."

Surely there must be a closer option?"

Bret just grins in the particular way he does, and drops the reminder. "Was it not you ralfy, who said that Kearvaig is your fantasy bothy?

The furthest far-away-place and where you most wanted to have a fireside whisky night?

. . . under the stars, with the northern lights, and the stags roaring up in the hills?"

"Well then," he concludes, "If we don't do it now, we will never do it!"

I think, and then think some more, trying to explain my way south to somewhere more '*convenient*' but I can't, and he's right, and I would be a total pussy to chicken out. I sigh, and look at the map on the wall,

"Kearvaig it is then."

Eight weeks later, as the mid-September summer air turns cooler, and the rain turns colder, we pack my wee Nissan Micra car with food supplies, coal, wood, glasses and two bottles of whisky. The bike rack on the back of my small hatchback is well up to the job of supporting two rugged mountain bikes as I had bought the best one I could afford from the bike shop many years ago. As the clock ticks towards 5am, we drive off out of Glasgow along the M8 motorway.

Bret then drops the bomb, "We're picking up my mate from the station at Inverness, and I said we would be there at 9."

"Aw, thanks for letting me know mate," I reply sarcastically, "And will he have his own bottle of whisky . . . or will he just be scoffing ours?"

"You will like him." confides my friend.

By the time we're passing Stirling the rain begins to hit the windscreen, and by the time we reach Pitlochry, the heavens open in a down-pour. The sky is dark and ominous with deep-grey cloud, like it means to stay for the day. We chat, we laugh, I relate some funeral situations, I tell him about Ginger Gray, and Boaby's dilemma. Bret laughs himself silly. We stop at

Aviemore to stretch out legs a bit, and then onwards we head to Inverness where I will be meeting 'Jim' for the first time. From what Bret tells me, he sounds quite a character.

The A9 road, running like an artery up the centre of Scotland, is awash with road works, with signs every few miles advising speed limits and delays, but fortunately, it is not yet the September holiday weekend, so we don't have traffic, or traffic police troubles.

I park up down a side street as Bret goes to pick up Jim from the station, and the two return within five minutes, thanks to detailed communication between the two a few days previous.

Jim is tall, lanky, red hair, short cropped, slightly rough, and with a loud, Glaswegian accent that I place around Easterhouse, or Castlemilk, somewhere south and east.

I am right, Jim is originally from Easterhouse, and now works around Scotland helping organise adventure and 'out doors' weekends, camps and such, for inner city youths.

He is rough mannered, sweary, direct and says what he means.

I like him immediately, although, I'm also mindful that with a few whiskies in him he could be different in all the wrong ways.

It has happened before with others.

After strapping Jim's bike as best I can onto the rack, we head off, a little slower this time, across to Ullapool, then north onto much quieter roads, narrow, winding and needing constant drivers vigilance. It's a long and wet three hour drive and we are relieved to get out of the small car and stretch our legs at the Cape Wrath Ferry, where we wait patiently with our bikes now loaded up, and our wet-gear on for the small ferry to take us across the Kyle of Durness and further into the wilderness.

The ferry is small, very small, but as it is quiet and as it is mid-week, we have the journey across the water to ourselves. I tip the ferryman, and take his phone number for the return pick-up the following afternoon. It's almost 2 in the afternoon now and we still have a good few miles to go on our bikes, over slippy wet rocks and gaps in the heather that used to be pathways. It's hard going to start with, but we get into the mood a bit more as the rain drenching clouds above us part to reveal blue sky and a warmer, drying breeze from the north. After we get past the two lochs, we are downhill most of the way, with the single track road getting easier on our bicycles, and in the distance we can sense the detached tranquillity of our destination.

We hear the sea, we smell the shore line, we taste salt air on our lips, and we see the golden sands of Kearvaig bay sparkle in the bright sunlight now sweeping across the incredible landscape in front of us, and then we spy the small, isolated whitewashed cottage standing stoically in open ground, just above the shore line.

We have arrived.

To make the best of the remains of the day, Bret, Jim and myself immediately get busy, Jim, building a fire in the bothy fireplace, Bret unpacking sleeping bags and laying out what's needed for a good night's sleep, and I get the burner on for a pot of tea, and sort out biscuits and sandwiches.

The weather remains dry, golden and beautiful, with the chill from the wetting autumnal rain having passed and gone. We have a good meal as the sun sinks down over the Atlantic, and Jim pulls out a tin flute which he plays well, and it creates more positive mood for our night ahead.

In the glowing embers of the day as night rolls across the hills around us, we open our bottles of whisky and pour our first drams.

A cadenheads Glen Lochy and an older official version of Lagavulin, sherry matured.

Kearvaig seems to kick the whisky in our glasses alive like no other location can do.

The alcohol is magnificent, and so is this location.

Jim lights a splif, a large one, best of gear.

Bret farts, and Jim and I complain.

I pour more tea.

Jim starts to laugh, and Bret complains, and we all laugh, then Jim asks for a story about funerals and whisky, so I tell a story and they laugh.

We chat away the remains of the day, then the three of us go for a midnight swim in the ocean which sobers us up for more whisky which then accompanies us into the dark small hours of a bright new day.

We are in an enchanted place and we feel its presence embracing us.

In the midst of the night, green light flickers high across the sky above, dancing and rolling like ocean waves, bright and vivid to our night ajusted vision, we witness a great drama of nature until, at last, exhausted and drunk, we fall asleep around the fire place, tucked up, and cosy in our sleeping bags.

I love this bothy, I love all the bothies, and they are always the best places for whisky, being basic, elemental, devoid of pretension or vanity, and full of honest character.

Keep your fancy bars, and your gentlemens lounges, they are comfortable and pedestrian, it can only ever be a bothy for me.

Chapter Twelve - Acquaintances of the Undertakers' Stash

Father Chomley, servant of god.

…The priest at Our Lady Of Innocence in Dennistoun is a god-fearing man, and encourages all his parishioners to fear God too by setting a personal example by virtue of the man of god that he is. He is a loyal fan of the God of the Old Testament. Jehovah is his God, although he prefers to refer to him as Yahweh out of respect for tradition. He has no time for the more cuddly God as endorsed by Jesus, the loving God, the caring God, the soft and forgiving God who only wants us all to love him, and to love us in return.

Father Chomley has no time for that sort of God.

His God is smiting, vengeful, angry, unforgiving, nasty, proud, conceited, and cruel.

His God demands sacrifice, the slaughter of his enemies, the constant fear of his believers and unrelenting loyalty of all who worship him on pain of death and damnation.

And as a disciple of this God, Father Chomley is unwavering in the enthusiasm and dedication he brings to his calling as a parish priest.

All his parishioners are in fear of him and his temper, which is just the way it should be.

We arrive with the hearse on a gentle summers evening well ahead of reception time for the receiving into church of the mortal remains of an old lady. The family have arrived, and are clearly well organised, having four young bearers ready to assist carrying the coffin into church once the priest is ready.

But I know how he works, I know how this priest manipulates and ridicules. I wander quietly down to the sacristy and stand silently outside, keeping still as Father Chomley berates a parishioner for not attending confession enough. She is now in tears as he angrily rebukes her for her sins.

Then, suddenly, accompanied by his pass-keeper and altar-server, he breezes out into the church.

"Good evening Father," I say. "Do you wish the flowers below the altar or at the back of the church?"

He pauses, caught off-guard, considering the option. "Altar" he spits, continuing, "Be quick, I'm busy tonight, meeting with the bishop at 8pm". I nod briefly to the hearse driver, standing ready at the top of the steps into the church, and with a floral spray in each hand, he deposits them both, with dignity, on the steps below the altar about seven feet apart. "NO, NO, NO," thunders Father Chomley, "Further apart! Do you really want me to trip over that when I'm blessing the coffin?" he demands angrily. I remain silent and passive, which annoys him further, and we proceed to the front door to receive the coffin into mass and vigil.

Father Chomley beckons across the main mourner. "Give the money to me in a plain white envelope tomorrow after mass," he stipulates. She bows her head meekly in obedience to the disciple of the God of fear and anger.

We proceed into the church, then, as the hearse driver and myself head off back to the garage, I think about what Jesus would think of this man.

Malcolm the murderer

Malcolm murdered his first victim when he was only sixteen. He drove the stolen car he was driving into a suspected police informant crushing him between the car and a brick wall. This was when Malcolm made his reputation as a hard man. Thereafter, he looked after it carefully by regular bouts of assault, theft and thereafter, time in Barlinnie prison. After an argument in custody, he was attacked and stabbed which caused him to relapse into a coma for several weeks. Once recovered, he was worse than before, cold, violent, insular and bitter.

The only one that Malcolm loved was his mother. He was an only child to a single parent. She was light and hope in life. When she was diagnosed with lung cancer, he was the only one available to look after her in the last few months. He took himself out of society and hid away in her house, looking after her, cleaning, making meals, watching telly, and sleeping beside her in bed to provide comfort to her.

His absence also let things cool down a bit in the streets. He had recently stabbed a junkie over a 12 inch pizza. The young lad was left in a wheelchair. It did not go down well in the local community.

Malcolm looks across the room at me with a cold intense stare. I am sitting in the front room of his mothers house making arrangements for her funeral.

"Ma Mam was an angel, and I want the best for her." he states.

"Money's not a problem here mate," he adds, just so as I would know.

We slowly make arrangements, detailed and specific, as he has thought it through carefully, telling his mum that she would have a funeral fit for a queen. She said it made her happy. She had been a simple woman, doing her best, keeping her life humble as befitted her circumstance in life.

Throughout Malcom's violent career, she remained supportive. She did all she could, but Malcolm had other plans. He was laying beside her in bed the night she died, she suddenly reached out and grasped his hand, firmly, as if strong again, and whispered that angels and golden light were all around her, and singing and joy and love, and that she needed to go away with the angels, and it was all right, it was peaceful, joyful and wonderful. Malcolm tells me this, as if looking for a confessor, a witness, an explanation. When he had last nearly died, all he experienced was cold, dark, an abyss, a deep, deep loss of everything.

The joy in her passing terrified him

Doctor Midazolam

Some of the nursing staff found the Doctor to be a bit strange. He was, in their opinion, distant and cold despite being civil, polite, and clearly a respected medical professional at the top of his career. There was never any issues with him doing 'inappropriate' things to patients. Nothing of a 'bad' nature that would be a cause for concern, however, he was known to be uncommunicative with staff, even his seniors, but that did not seem to impact on his career.

After several years advancing in his profession, he opted to stick to the role of a medical registrar, specialising in palliative care, for which he seemed to have an affinity and a certain professional manner. He was highly regarded by his peers and seniors as being the 'right sort' for the vocation and as he 'walked the walk' as well as 'talking the talk', they let him get on with it, after all, there was growing demand in society for palliative care, which many hospices found to be both rewarding and lucrative.

Cancer charities always make big money, and all tax-free too, with V.A.T. requirements set at 5% instead of the usual rate. The Doctor opined on several occasions that 'both cancer and fluffy animals will always get people to open their purses'. The pharmaceutical industry had identified decades ago that medical care sales near 'end of life' were most profitable along with vaccines, and subsequent earnings declarations would keep investors quiet.

The Doctor loved to visit his hospices, where he could quietly talk through 'end of living' care with distressed relatives and reassure them that there would be 'no pain' which they inevitably found to be very comforting. The Doctor had an impressive array of options available to him in terms of medications and drugs. Morphine was always reliable. Steroids very useful. Haloperidol was an option, but not his favourite. He found Dexamethasone to be a bit too *'encouraging'*, so recommended against its use on the grounds that it would create false expectations. Benzodiazepines were frequently used where symptoms were refractory. He kept a large supply of the drug he favoured the most. He knew all the options, he knew what he was doing.

The doctor kept a diary. Personal, hidden in a shelf of his library at home, in the room that his wife and daughters were forbidden to enter. It listed all his patients over the years who he had helped find comfort in their last moments of suffering. He liked to be the one who transformed suffering into a calm relaxed termination of life. He liked to record their last witnessed words as they passed on. He liked to record the distressed comments of relatives. It felt important.

Some nurses found him a bit creepy, however, they would not risk saying so out loud as the Doctor was a highly respected medical professional, appreciated by society and always generous in supporting worthy causes, and as such, was personally acquainted of well-placed and influential people within the community.

Seeing old Hughie again.

It's a sunny, breezy spring day in May as we leave the parlour in Springburn, and head up the road to collect ashes at Glasgow Crematorium. Things have settled down with the volume of work now as the last of the winter business subsides into quieter days with less pressure of workload. Jiffy is driving the van, and we are talking motorbikes, especially motorbike shows such as the one at Edinburgh which took place again last month in March. Jiffy, being a proper biker always goes. I went this year, but thought it to be poor value for money. A coffee and simple burger had cost £8.50.

We discuss the pretentious bastards at the Harley Davidson 'enclosure' who are show-boating and looking like cookie-cutter clones of Americana. They really were right up their own arse.

The bric-a-brac stalls are the best bit of the show where some old relics and nostalgia items can still be found for reasonable money, but even these bargains are fading away now with the arrival of the internet.

Suddenly I see someone across the road on Hawthorn Street that I recognise. Its Hughie the old hearse driver, retired for about a year now, and away from the rat-race of the daily grind. As Jiffy stops the van, I jump out, checking for traffic as I navigate the road across to where Hughie is walking along slowly. I catch up with him just at the corner of Frenbank Street, opposite the Salvation Army Hall. I call out his name. He stops, looks up, towards me. He does not recognise me. I am shocked. "Hughie mate, Uncle Fester, it's me, ralfy, from work, remember?" He does not seem to remember. Hughie looks old, gray, tired, shrunken, and exhausted.

My heart sinks, and I try to explain. "Hughie, we worked together for over fifteen years mate! I was always out on the hearse with you doing funerals and stuff, do you remember now?"

A glint appears in his tired eyes as recollection awakens from deep within his memory, almost forgotten now it appears, in the mists of time.

"Aye, son, you were always good to me, buying me rolls and tea out on the jobs."

I do most of the talking, which is not for very long, as I can see that Hughie is now a shadow of his former self and it is painful to see. His cigarette habit has taken its toll now, smoking twenty a day since the moment he left school and started working with the Co-op as a delivery boy. Time has caught up with Hughie, and it shows. He tells me that he is going to Blackpool for the weekend, on a community bus arranged by the Ladies up in Balgrayhill flats who arrange days out for the pensioners in the community. The bus leaves on Friday and returns on Monday so it will be almost like a full week's holiday.

He hopes it will be sunny.

I head back to the waiting van, depressed and hurt.

Jiffy tells me it happens all the time with people.

3 Sisters.

Marjorie was a successful woman when she died, suddenly, at the age of 70. She had worked in the office at a garden centre which, under new ownership, grew and became very successful attracting awards and recognition from the horticultural community across the County. Marjorie was well rewarded for her loyalty and spent all her spare time and money on her three lovely daughters. They all grew up to be successful, well-off people with good husbands.

The youngest daughter was the first to be informed of her 'passing', and proceeded to arrange a burial at the local cemetery, not far from her late mother's last home address. As she had no choice, she informed, by e-mail her two older sisters. The middle sister replied first, asking who had the inventory of her mother's flat contents. The oldest, and richest sister informed her two younger sisters that the proposed cemetery was 'shabby' and not suitable for her mother.

The youngest sister complained to the middle sister who asked again for a full inventory of her mother's flats contents as there were items of 'sentimental value'. The youngest sister e-mailed the oldest sister to make it clear that the burial would go ahead as she was paying for it. The oldest sister arranged a lawyer's response advising that the funeral be cancelled until a resolution had been agreed by the three sisters.

The middle sister advised that there should be no sale of her mother's flat as it was currently 'too much of a buyers' market'. The youngest sister visited a lawyer then proceeded with the funeral against her oldest sisters wishes. Only the youngest sister attended the funeral. The oldest sister thereafter demanded an exhumation as she had evidence that the 'wishes' of her mother had been ignored.

The youngest sister sold her mother's flat and auctioned all the contents then refused to share the money with her older sisters unless they left things as they were. The middle sister sent a lawyers letter demanding a third of all monies. The oldest sisters presented evidence that the 'wishes' of her late mother had been ignored and this was upheld in a civil court and the youngest sister was forced to arrange an exhumation, with a subsequent re-burial in a small rural cemetery near to where the oldest sister lived.

The middle sister demanded money for her 'trauma' and 'hurt' but received nothing.

A private investigator, hired by the youngest daughter discovered that the 'wishes' evidence submitted to the civil court by the oldest sister were professionally faked. The youngest sister sued the oldest sister in a civil action and won.

Their mother was then exhumed and cremated at the local crematorium with the ashes separated equally into three metal urns and delivered by courier to each of the three sisters. All their inheritance, and more, was spent on lawyers fees, exhumations, and a cremation.

There was nothing left.

Brother Norbert.

I have a funeral to conduct today, direct to Glasgow Crematorium, with only a few, immediate members of the family attending. They did not want a church reception or mass as they were no longer practicing Catholics, but they are still Catholics by identity. They did not want to fake it for formality.

Their local priest agrees, however he is not comfortable with a humanist officiant being hired to say a few words at the committal. Joan in the parlour at Mansfield Street phones Brother Norbert. A retired monk, he agrees unconditionally to take a small, brief service for the family, and the matter is resolved.

We uplift Brother Norbert from his retreat in Partickhill Road, a quiet, secluded spot where he has retired after years spent in Africa, helping the poor, then being imprisoned by the rich. It's the west-end, so nobody seems to mind that a hearse with a coffin stops at the side of the road and picks up a passenger. He is a small man, slightly built, humble and civil, just the way a mature monk should look.

I sit in the rear seat of the hearse beside the foot of the coffin, whilst Brother Norbert occupies the passenger seat beside little Ted who is driving the hearse today. I ask him how he's getting on. He says he's fine and looking forward to a weekends retreat down in Largs, where he sometimes helps out. He says that a 'lot of forgiveness needs to be earned' and that 'evil surrounds goodness to empower itself'. Both Ted and I notice a slight edge in his usually mild-mannered dialogue. Brother Norbert sighs, then opens his bible to read. This is his 'do not disturb' sign, and we both respect his wishes.

We drive carefully up Hyndland Road towards Glasgow Crematorium, and within ten minutes arrive at the new chapel, small and intimate, where three members of the family await our arrival with a small bunch of seasonal flowers to go on top of the coffin. Brother Norbert leads us in, then after blessing the coffin with holy water, proceeds with his service. It will take no longer than fifteen minutes.

Outside, in the warming May sunshine, little Ted and I get chatting to Bill, the attendant. We talk about Brother Norbert. "A quiet little man, living a simple quiet life," I say, "And in a nice bit of the west-end too, handy for the pubs."

Bill laughs, "Oh! . . . you won't see him out and about, no way, my sister lives across the road from him and says she has all the history, he's one that keeps himself to himself, and no wonder with all that's happened in his life!" Little Ted and I are all ears. "Apparently he was out in Nigeria with the Marists in the nineteen-sixties, and got arrested and beaten for trying to feed the Biafran war refugees," says Bill, adding "and when he eventually survived that and got back to Scotland, he then allegedly had to deal with the child abuse situation happening at the St Columba's residential home down in Largs, which was a huge scandal at the time. It was said that Brother Norbert had to go through the wringer trying to deal with it as best he could, and to limit the damage to the order. It all goes to show that the best of people can find themselves in the worst of situations, and then they have to survive and maintain some dignity."

"You know," continues Bill, "Victims of crimes are often not just the immediate victims, but also those around them that are trying to do good." The service has ended, and we are heading back down to Partick to drop off Brother Norbert. He is reading his bible.

Little Ted and I are silent, deep in our own thoughts.

The Swansons.

The Swansons are a very well-known family within the village of Torrence, laying just north, and only a mile outside of Glasgow. The old mother has recently died, and as a well-known figure around the village, will be missed. Her immediate family especially, are very upset and arrange to give her a very special send-off. She lived to a ripe old age of 90, and the family, who are into theatre, the arts and media, are going to make the funeral a day to remember.

'A lot of people will be attending,' we are told.

'A police escort will be needed from the house to the cemetery,' we are told.

'Just turn up with a hearse and three cars and we will do the rest,' we are told.

It is my funeral week, in my area, so I just have to get on with it. Billy Flannigan, the hearse driver and I leave in good time and head to the parlour in Springburn to collect the coffin. The viewing room has been stuffed with flowers, about 30 of them, and we can hardly fit them all into the hearse so have to use the boots of the family limousines to hold the smaller bouquets.

John is still burning from the 'telling-off' he got from the police Inspector after he phoned for a family escort. "And just who is going to pay for a police outrider?" demanded the Inspector. The police escort never materialises, and the Swansons were not that bothered anyways.

We leave as a cortege from the door of the deceased's house, late due to traffic congestion and yet more flowers to be stuffed into the back of the hearse. The family have decorated the front door of her house with flowers and a large sign saying 'Home Sweet Home'.

As we arrive at Cadder Cemetery the rain starts to come on, and with the Church of Scotland minister looking on with some trepidation, the family commence their theatre. First, the white dove release, where the startled doves fly away in different directions chased by angry black crows nesting in the trees above.

Second, the soloist, a very nervous granddaughter who gargles through a rendition of 'Amazing Grace' accompanied by a guitarist who fumbles his chords as the guitar is getting wet in the rain.

Third, a balloon release, one for each year of her life, so ninety large balloons are let go, not separately, but all together as the retaining strings have got fankled. The wind blows the balloons, en masse, over the cemetery wall and onto the road beyond, causing a multi-vehicle crash.

Forth, a poem is read by the deceased's eldest son, who cries and howls all the way through it so nobody can hear the words.

Fifth, a brief committal by the clergyman, who keeps it short and sweet as many assembled family burst into open wailing and howling.

Sixth, family members take turns in shovelling back the soil and gravel into the grave whilst the diggers look on in amusement.

Seventh, a lectern and memorial book are produced out the back of a car and mourners invited to sign it, despite the pages of the fancy-looking book rapidly becoming soggy and then ripping due to the increased ferocity of the rain and wind.

Eighth, a prolonged thank you and 'few words' from the eldest daughter which take over ten minutes, because she wants to relate a 'funny story' about her 'darling, darling mummy.'

Ninth, a granite composite vase plinth appears out the back of a van and is carried by four men over to the graveside before being dumped at the foot of the grave. "If you move that stone vase boys!" states one of the family to the grave diggers, "I will come back and shoot you." All this, whilst other family members fill the vase with as many flowers as they can cram into it.

Tenth, a collective sing-song from all the attending mourners of Vera Lynn's 'We'll Meet Again' with sheet music and words for those who don't know the lyrics. All verses are sung as best people can manage.

The diggers look on in fascination, mixed with a frustration at getting soaked in the rain along with the Swansons and their friends. At last, it is finally all over now. The three limousines breeze off in the heavy rain towards the city centre where a 'festival' has been arranged.

Billy and I are the last to leave, and as the hearse rolls on back down the road to Springburn, I turn to Billy the hearse driver and ask him, "What the fuck was all that about?"

Billy just laughs, then lights a cigarette, "Fuck knows!" he replies.

A Humble man.

The house is clean, bright, fresh and bare of anything but essentials. A comfy armchair, a side table with mug stains into the wood, an old gas fireplace, with original tile mantelpiece from the time that coal burned within the grate.

A home-help tidies up a bit, but there's not much left to tidy. She gives me the paperwork required for the old man's funeral. I pause reflectively in the silence of the quiet home, standing in a corner of an estate somewhere, nowhere in particular, in a city like most others.

His life has moved on, and this is all that's left behind within the silence of a bright new day.

This moment here.

This moment here and now.

10 to 10.

When Mister Munro passed away all his clocks stopped in the house. Precisely at the moment, the exact moment, that he passed away. His wife Maureen did not know what to make of it. This is why she is asking my opinion, after all, I am an undertaker, and she presumes that I know all about these things because of what I do.

Having many years' experience as an undertaker, in and out of many people's houses, this home is nothing of noteworthiness. It is well furnished, all quality and basic furniture, and we are sitting together in the kitchen again after I have been through to the late Mr Munro's workshop to see all of his collection of mechanical clocks have stopped, all of them, at exactly the same time, all two hundred of them. Maureen told me how many clock there were, after all she knew as she had to live with them in the house, all of them, making a racket all day every day.

She got used to their presence, but never liked the noise of all the ticking, it drove her daft until her husband made a workshop for them at the back of the utility room and a bit out of the way. He died quietly at the hospital, in the late evening, at 10 minutes past 10pm. Maureen showed me the cremation form and death certificate she had received from the nurse. Sure enough, time of death on the form was 22.10. This was the time at which all his clocks stopped.

The kitchen clock is still ticking silently away on the wall, stating 11.15am. Maureen wonders why that particular clock is still ticking. I ask her if it's the one she uses to keep time. She says yes, that's the one. I suggest that it is her late husband's way of saying she should just get on with her life. Maureen ponders what I'm saying, becoming emotional, but regaining her composure as the meaning of what I'm suggesting sinks in. I elaborate a little, suggesting that all *his* clocks have stopped as a sign of respect, but *her* clock is still ticking because she has many years ahead of her. I suggest that the ten past ten time is a smile from the clock hands. She laughs gently, registering the more positive sentiment of what I'm saying, and wiping tears from her eyes with a small paper tissue, agrees that she must be strong and that life must go on.

She will find good homes for all his clocks, and keep her kitchen clock, as it is now the most important one in her life.

George the Driver.

George Thomson started working at the Co-op as soon as he left school at the age of eleven years in 1944. He was a small lad, even for his age, so was assigned to help a milkman on his rounds, delivering milk and bread rolls from the Cowlairs Dairy in Springburn. The milkman drove the cart which was pulled by a small horse saved from a life working in coal mines, and George did the running from doorstep to doorstep dropping off the milk and rolls as ordered. He quickly settled in as his mother made sure he was never late, and was always polite to customers as well as those he worked with. As he never dropped any of the milk bottles, or stole any bread rolls, he was well thought of and never needed to look for another employer again. He always made time for the horse, grooming it and treating it with carrots, and sometimes mints.

154

In the 1960's when the demand for delivered milk was falling, and the Cities population beginning to decline, George volunteered to transfer to the Funeral Service, as demand was growing locally for funerals. George drove limousines for the next forty years. As a funeral director, I could never fault George whilst on funerals. He was attentive, professional, sympathetic to families and courteous. Proper old school, and with self-respect, a real gent.

His limousine was always immaculate, with clean windows, proper maintained interiors, and a freshness that came from proper ventilation, and not chemical sprays. He would wax the veneer on his dashboard, giving it an additional shine that no other limousine could match.

It's now 2008 and George has reduced his working hours to 'part-time' just to boost his company pension a little bit further, and to ensure that he does not stop working 'suddenly'.

Out on the car wash at Shieldhall we get chatting on a weekday afternoon, during the calm of a soft summer's day, with autumn not far ahead of us. "How are you doin' George y'old trooper?" I ask. George looks up from shammy-ing his vehicle dry, having just washed it. I catch his eye, and swiftly adopt a more sombre tone. "What's up mate, you look miserable, even more than usual?"

"I finish up at the end of the week, that's me done now. You won't be seeing me again." he states. "And are they giving you a send-off?" I ask, thinking that the other drivers have organised a cake or something. "No, I asked them not to, I don't want any fuss, but a few lads are coming out to the Bowling Club at Robroyston. I've arranged a wee meal and game of bowls for them." He pauses, reflecting, then adds, "I do the flower beds, every year, at the bowling green, and people come to see them that aren't even into the bowling." I pause, thinking, "And is your employer marking the occasion with a presentation for long service, why, it must be over 50 years by now!"

"62 years in total"' replies George, "And none of the managers have approached me to say goodbye, or anything."

There is a silence between us for a few seconds.

"At least they are being honest with you George." I suggest. He pauses, reflecting, "You're only a number to them these days, they just don't care like they did in the old days." "Your right", I affirm, "When *I* leave, I will just go, silently, suddenly, with no warning."

The following day, I catch George by the wash bay again and give him a bottle of single malt whisky. "All the best George, and have a good retirement."

George smiles, says thanks, we shake hands, and I feel it's the beginning of the end of my time as an undertaker. I just know I will be leaving within a few more years. For good.

Chapter Thirteen - Whisky and a devil

Glasgow's Whisky Club is having another Wednesday meet at the Bon Accord, but to be honest, my heart is just not in it. Too much has changed too fast and too significantly. New members are forming affable cliques, old members are remaining good company, but something *feels* different.

I sense the winds of change are blowing through the club in North Street, Charing Cross. It is one of the subtle skills in life, knowing when it's time to move on. I think that if we allow our 'present' to remain unchallenged by apathy, routine and laziness, we drift further and further into the past. I have seen this happen to so many old people over the years, due, of course, to my job. A job that no one wants but somebody has to do. I do it, and I have no regrets. It has been a fascinating tapestry over the last two decades . . . of humanity and humanities condition.

I see it tonight in the club, the genuinely interested, the habitual drinkers, and the unique whisky-scene cheer of gossip, analysis and rumour which fuels conversations along with copious amounts of whisky. Most people want to know the next important story, what's 'collectable' now, how will Daftmill work out, is Bruichladdich doing anything special these days, have Springbank announced their next release date yet, and has anyone tried a sample of the 12yo cask strength, rumour says that 'influencers' are getting samples from Springbank.

My fellow whisky-clubbers ask me . . . but I never receive any samples, and I have made it clear that I don't want to either. My whisky channel is growing on YouTube, so I must be doing something right, I suspect it's just because I give *my* opinion, . . . and nobody else's script. An opinion is only an opinion. For those 'influencers' who want it, there are *gifts* to be received, on an *understanding* . . . you understand.

It's the lay of the land. Traditional journalists get more; they are further up the pecking order. Hospitality, expenses, bottles, invitations. It's all part of the business of looking after business. I get it. I remain independent; it's an *undertakers* thing.

What the Industry simply does not grasp is the future effect of the internet and how online activity will determine the success or failure of brand in the future. Senior decision makers are in ivory towers. They want more sales, but they don't want things to change. They represent a microcosm of British Society in the early 2000's clinging to versions of the past, the 'advantage' of empire and the *City* in London, of societies and 'clubs', its' class and culture.

Britain is in for a shock over the next few years, and nobody wants to hear about it. It's a cultural, heritage, delusional thing. Britain does this so well. It thinks its past is its future. Decisions makers cut production costs to make savings, and then reduce staff costs where they can. They buy too much 'marketing', and hire well-spoken actors who know the moves, and know how to make the moves, all in lockstep. All the *same*.

Many new-made spirits will die in the tired inadequate 'casks' in which they were sent to die. They already are, and the pretty words of Industry conversation, 'heritage', and even the enthusiasm of enthusiastic aficionados will not save them.

Some businesses will see the signs, and adapt, adjust, change, and survive.

Others will be bought up or fade away.

It's a global village now.

I must find me a bothy, somewhere quiet, and get out of the way. I don't want to be around as the defences fall.

I must have been drinking! It must have been the day before a day off work, when I generally allow myself more malt-moments, more alcohol, and more gentle inebriation. When Orlando the orange cat starts purring and stretching by the fireside, I know it is time to pull the blanket over my head and rest comfortably on the pillow, on the carpet, by the fireside.

It's raining outside, and as winter begins to arrive, I feel the coldness of the end of summer again, and looking into the glowing embers of smoking coal nestled within the fire grate I feel warmed a little more, and then a little bit more, and it really is getting quite hot.

It's a big bright sun, shimmering across the river Nile and I am in my works uniform, including top hat, and with my conducting cane, and am ascending the steps of the Temple of Sobek, crocodile god of the Egyptians. The god of plenty, of learning, of living water, of medicine and healing. Sobek stands at the door to his temple. Tall, large, imposing and very strange. ". . . and do you mortal creature choose to harm the innocent?" he asks loudly. "No," I reply, "I choose to serve all who need my services, and offer no judgement. I do the best I can."

"and do you make mistakes?" demands Sobek, his eyes glowing iridescent blue.

"Yes, a few, and none out of malice," I reply.

"Then enter, servant of Anubis!"

Sobek lifts his staff, makes the sign of the 'enhh', and with a wave bids me enter his house.

I enter the temple; it is calm and cool inside, with large tapestries swaying gently against the walls, relating in their infinite threads the journey of the gods from the stars above to the place called planet earth. Anubis welcomes me with a nod, and tells me that I have done well in my tasks. I apologise for my occasional mistakes in getting arrangements wrong, but over the years they have been few and far between, and Anubis acknowledges them justly. "Even gods make mistakes," he tells me. "You have done well and now you must leave what you're doing and attend to another task that I have for you."

"What is that?" I ask.

"To find the Book of brilliant things, and to make real the words that bring victory in a realm you cannot visit, but will see clearly." I nod my obedience, although I do feel that it's all a bit cryptic and odd, and that I just don't understand it. Anubis and Sobek are joined now by Thoth, and in front of the altar, they come together and make the sign of 'the three and one'.

I feel emotional, a sense of something lost in order to let something else be found. I hear time sigh through the temple stones, and I see the stars twinkle bright through the open door of the temple, I smell the myrrh and kapet mingling together and intense. I see, for just a moment, everything I can comprehend, and it is beautiful and powerful to behold, and then I understand that death needs life, but life does not need death.

It is time now, for me to leave. At the foot of the temple steps where they meet the Sahara sand, a small devil sits crying. It looks like a goblin should, with small stubby horns and a long swishy tail, leathery and scarred. Some dark bird feathers surround his neck like a necklace, and he is clearly distressed. I stop and ask what is wrong.

He tells me that his punishment from the gods is to count every grain of sand that surrounds the temple. That is a lot of sand to count. I hand him a whisky glass from out of my pocket and tell him it is blessed. He takes it, looking at me puzzled and suspicious. I take back the glass briefly, place it in the sand and fill it to the brim. I brush the fill-level to the rim of the glass with a feather I see laying nearby, then pour it onto a temple step. "Now count only the grains of sand from the glass, and then every time you fill the glass again, you will know how many grains of sand there are in it. This will speed things up for you."

The small devil thanks me, and quickly proceeds with his task. I walk away to sit by the Nile, the night is cool, calm and clear with a sea of stars burning brightly in the firmament above. I sit on a rock by the river, and listen to the wind, after all, there is no rush now to return to my fireside.

I have permission from Anubis to linger and enjoy this moment by the river for a little longer.

I have earned it.

Chapter Fourteen - Leaving my job and finding a bothy

As soon as I had phoned my dear old mother on one anonymous Thursday evening, much like most other Thursday evenings, I realised that I would have to leave work, sell my house, and move out of Scotland and over to the Isle of Man to look after her. I could just tell in her voice, her struggle to think clearly and in her breezy denial, that she needed help and could no longer live on her own without support.

It is a classic case where a small decision has a huge impact on life. It will make perfect sense, not to let her be taken into a care home, which would cost £1,000 a week, but also, if she died shortly thereafter, I would owe the U.K. tax authorities about £200,000 in inheritance tax, due to the rules being the rules. With taxation and loss of inheritance value, along with the loss of her pension and life savings disappearing into care home costs, it would mean that I would be working at the Co-op for the equivalent of twenty years . . . for no money.

You see my situation?

Ridiculous.

Absurd.

It's a no-brainer.

I will have to dramatically change my life to give her a little more of her life back to her. It is the right thing to do for both of us. It is not just for financial reasons. I want to care for her as I know I will do a better job than institutions can do. I think about explaining the situation to my boss at work but there really is just no point. There are currently redundancies on offer, and good money severances too, but on enquiry with the manager I am told in no uncertain terms, 'we don't plan to let valuable staff go!' I ask why. "Because you'll take the money then probably go and work for a competitor being fully qualified and experienced, or start out on your own."

"Thanks for letting me know I'm valuable anyway," I respond, then head out of his office to find a task or something else to do.

I'm raging.

The manager sits in his office, content in the belief that I will stay as I do not appear to have any other options. He's wrong.

As usual, the best way to get paid off with a good lump sum is to be incompetent and not 'valuable'. That's life, good fortune can often favour the undeserving.

There's a job for me on the office desk. As it turns out it will be the last arrangement that I ever make.

––––––––––––––––––

An old lady, one of the high flats in Cowcaddens, her late husband is in the Royal Infirmary mortuary. I phone her and arrange a suitable time to visit. "9th Floor," she tells me, "So don't bother taking the stairs, the lift will be quicker and I've checked that it works today." she adds before hanging up.

It's Block 2, in Stewart Street, and after the lift clunks and grinds its way to the ninth floor, I stare out of the landing window for a few minutes, out, across and over the city below me, enjoying the peacefulness and the panoramic view, shivering as I acknowledge quietly to myself that this is my last arrangement . . . ever.

Within the week I will be gone. It will be suddenly all behind me. It feels weird, and for now, only I know, like something is *changing*. Fate and happenstance.

I ring the bell on a brightly painted door in a clean and cheerful landing, and almost immediately an elderly woman, thin, small and exuding a bubbly and charming positivity answers the door and beckons me in with a flourish of the oven towel still in her hand.

"A wee cup of tea son, and a fresh bake scone?"

"Thank you very much Mrs Twindell, very kind of you."

She leads me through to her front room and beckons me to an armchair by the window with a clip-on plastic tray for holding tea and scones and other such things. The kettle is already boiling as a large fresh scone; still oven-warm is placed before me on a floral printed plate, dripping in melting butter and raspberry jam. The room is cosy, despite being sparse and with mostly basic furnishings. A bright and slightly gaudy painting of a tropical sunset hangs on one of the walls. Mrs Twindell sees me looking at it.

"Painted that myself . . . studied art at the College up the road, evening classes, loved it. Now, anyway, I want a simple funeral for my husband, nothing fancy, so no fancy coffin, no notice in the papers, and a small spray of colourful flowers will do, and I won't be viewing, so just a basic light coffin, and my neighbour will say a few words at the graveside so no vicar, and I have the deeds to the lair and it's the last internment because I'm being cremated and will go into the lair, eventually, as a wee box of ashes."

I note down Mrs Twindells commands.

The arrangement is completed in less than ten minutes. She knows exactly what she wants. "Do you want another scone son?" she enquires. I am shocked that I finished it so quickly, but, anyway, it's my last ever arrangement, so I may as well . . . it would be rude to refuse. She seems to like me.

"Do you like doing your job?" she asks.

I say I do, it's varied and never boring.

"How long have you been doing your job?" she asks.

I say that I've done it now for 21 years.

"How many funerals have you arranged?" she asks.

I think for a few seconds before replying, and tell her it must be about 1,200. She laughs. "I bet you see lots of life in death and dying." she chuckles. "I suppose I do." I respond, with a grin.

We chat briskly for the next twenty minutes about this and that and the next thing, and as time marches on, I conclude our meeting just as I finish the second fresh-baked scone, which I make a point of eating more slowly. Out of curiosity, I as her what she intends to do next, when the funeral is completed. "Nothing!" she replies assuredly, "Just relax in my little tropical paradise and when I'm not doing that, help my friends at the Balgrayhill Ladies Club, help and support those who need it."

I smile, the merry widows at Balgrayhill have quite a presence within the wider community, and they seem to have done so for quite a while.

"Let me show you son . . . my little tropical paradise."

Mrs Twindell beckons me out of my comfy chair. I am curious, and follow her through to another room where, on opening the door, all that is inside is a fully assembled greenhouse, painted on the outside with palm trees, blue skies and yellow waves of sand round the base. It looks like actual sand has been mixed with the paint then smeared over the glass to look as realistically tropical as possible.

An infrared lamp stands above the sliding door of the construction, elevated to about seven feet high on a robust tripod, and pointing towards a painted glowing sun, under the apex of the roof. It is most peculiar, and fascinating. Mrs Twindell gestures me forward and slides open the door revealing a perfect reconstruction of what sitting on a beach in the Caribbean should look like from out of the travel brochures.

I peer inside, there's a deckchair, three potted plastic palm trees of varying heights, a small beach ball, a wicker chair, stuck at a slight angle into the loose sand which covers the entirety of the greenhouse floor, and the sound of calypso music emanating softly from a small speaker in the corner.

Suddenly, Mrs Twindell switches on the infrared light, which is soft but intense in the glow it provides to the interior.

The whole concept works a treat.

It looks amazing.

"My little hideaway!" declares the old woman, "Every day I go in and sit for an hour just to hear the music, chill-out, and to get me some sun. My husband bought it by mistake a year ago, just as his dementia was kicking-in, but rather than return it, I saw the potential, and we assembled it up together, took us three weeks, but we got there in the end. It's all mine now, so there's a bit more space for the sunshine inside."

The situation is most odd but inspired. It is something I will never forget.

I make plans immediately to buy me a greenhouse on the Isle of Man.

Back in the office, there is no sun to be seen, only grey skies, and all is gloomy as befits the current mood of the place with the threat of redundancies looming. Apparently, they are taking on more staff in the main office in Manchester to help manage the disposal of experienced staff who actually do the work in regional branches and hubs. Makes sense I suppose, in a convoluted and very British sort of way.

It's traditional. One of many reasons why Britain is in long-term decline.

I process the arrangement I have just made, and tidy up my locker before stopping for ten days holiday. I am off to the Isle of Man for the T.T. motorbike races, but before I go, there is another wee session at Glasgow's Whisky Club I need to attend. They know I'm leaving at the whisky club, and Bill, the chairperson makes a special announcement about it, presenting me, on behalf of the club, with a rather nice bottle of bourbon. It's a good raucous night with good whiskies and some emotional farewells from malt-mates I've got to know over the last ten years.

———————————————————————

Gathering up and moving 1,500 bottles of whisky, and other quality spirits is no easy, or light-weight task. Getting things organised takes my mind off the recent phone call from my ex-regional manager at Co-operative Funeralcare who has been pleading with me to stay. "Care homes have professional staff to look after relatives properly so let them do their job!" he tells me.

It's pathetic. At the conclusion of the call, he does have the courtesy to wish me all the best, but goes on to make it clear that 'there will no chance of a severance package'. No worries there, I already knew that would be the case.

I load the van with box after box of exotic bottles and hope I don't have a crash going down the motorway to the ferry at Heysham.

I don't, and after four runs to and from the Island, I have shifted all that needs to be moved. My house sells on the market within three weeks.

A few days later, once I know for sure that the house has definitely sold, I think about the people I've worked with over the years. Some of them, over twenty years, and I feel a pang of guilt at not giving them a chance to say 'cheerio', so I make a point of going back to Shieldhall one last time, just to say goodbye to everyone.

Some are genuinely upset at my leaving, some depressed at the impact of losing an experienced colleague, some are indifferent, a few are glad to see me go or they just don't care.

That's life.

The regional manager calls me into his office and begs me to reconsider. I explain the reason. I explain the costs of staying; I explain the pointlessness of earning a lot less than it would cost my mother to pay for her 'care'. He does not want to understand, but, he can't stop me leaving. I leave his office and go to look for Jiffy, who is in the kitchen contemplating the abyss before him, as he usually does. He wishes me good luck, then tells me he wants to leave too as he hates the place. He always has, but it does not matter much. I'm sure he will when he's ready.

I go into the staff room and hand over three boxes of Thorntons chocolates for everyone to get a share of. Everyone in the room wishes me 'all the best'. Most are sincere, some less so, and it shows. I don't judge them, they have a lot on their mind with the weak leadership decisions impacting the business, almost on a daily basis now.

I leave, and never return.

That afternoon, I sit outside the back of the house, and smoke a cigar. It feels like a weight has been lifted from my shoulders. Now the decision is made, and is irreversible, I can actually move on as there is no longer anything to hold me back, except for the ghosts of memories, people and places, which always remain, deep-set in memories, only waiting for the moment to be remembered again, later, suddenly, and for no obvious reason.

I call in on Margaret, to say goodbye. We chat, and she pours more tea, then our conversation gets deeper. It has been ten years now since the

Smiddy days, but recollections are fresh. Margaret is in her late eighties, and still looking well. She has never smoked, drinks moderately and never chose to marry, so life has preserved her a little better, and, her distrust of doctors has not been to her disadvantage. Margaret pauses, looking at me in a way I have witnessed on several occasions before, and then leans forward slightly to give me some news, lowering her voice in case anybody hears.

"Sanny came to us at the Spiritualist hall a few years back and delivered a message for Ella . . . his wife." She continues, now sure of my full attention. "Two of us went to her new address in Bearsden and gave her his message," there is a dramatic pause, "Well, she was shocked and upset and told us to leave immediately before she called the police. Then, about a month later, she was found dead on the local railway line.

A tragic situation, really is, just such a shame, 'specially after doing so well for herself, just walked off the platform at the local station and in front of a train, full of valium she was."

"What was Sanny's message then Margaret?" I ask to settle my curiosity. "Well," discloses Margaret, "It was . . . Don't trust Ruby, she's just like you Darlin'!"

We sit in silence for a moment. Our tea is getting cold. I make sure to give Margaret a bottle of Glenmorangie 10yo, which is now her favourite, and say goodbye. She has been a great neighbour, but we won't be keeping in touch.

The day before I finally leave to go to the Isle of Man, I have one more whisky-task to fulfil. A day trip to Campbeltown to visit Springbank Distillery, and to record a tour of the place, showing how they make, and mature their whiskies. They have three basic permutations of what they produce. 'Springbank' is the main version, two and a half times distilled and full of complexity. 'Longrow' is the more heavily peated version, whilst

'Hazelburn' is the triple distilled, unpeated option from this distillery, and is delicate yet substantial.

The daylight of a new day brings some soft sunshine from behind fluffy, scurrying clouds of sparkling white as I drive up Loch Lomond and round to Inverary where I stop briefly, looking over the old puffer Vital Spark as she sits, dispossessed in the pier on Loch Fyne. I feel a pang of nostalgia, and briefly consider taking a detour to Crinan where I met the folks a few years back who were restoring an old clyde puffer, but I change my mind back to the original plan. I have to prioritise my purpose.

As I enter the front gates of Springbank, I spy my host marching across to the office, and give him a shout. "Hey, Peter, you big chunk, how are you doing?" Peter Currie looks across, grinning, and a little wary.

"Ralfy! Welcome to Springbank. Are you ready for a tour, or will you be interviewing me in the shop, or somewhere else, or what?"

I have another plan.

With having such light, single camera equipment, I am thinking of a walk-through as this has not been done yet in video form online. A walk through from the beginning of the whisky-making process to the bottling process and then the shop. It will be full of bloopers and such, but I think that if anyone would be up to the challenge, it will be Peter, as he's a good egg!

I explain my plan.

He seems rather uncertain.

"What about the lack of light in the kilning area?" he asks. "Not a problem," I respond, "Let it be poorly lit, seeing as it's a poorly lit place anyway, so we can show the distillery naturally, without the cosmetic veneer that the BBC would do. There will be no editing, no deletions, no fake, just as is, so what do you say Peter?"

He rolls his eyes and agrees, unsure, but curious as to how it will work out. I assure him that if there is any video footage he objects to, it will not go online. That is my reassurance policy. Some 'makers' out there are taking liberties with their content as it is still the early days of the internet, and I am careful to keep my content sympathetic, if, at times, . . . critical. I keep

168

it dignified as best I can without looking like a sell-out. I leave that to some others. They can do it better than me.

The recordings are a protracted process covering seven, ten minute vlogs, and just as the camera batteries finally begin to fail, we conclude with a final chat in the Cadenheads tasting room. Peter seems a lot happier now. He has never done this sort of video theme before, and was wondering what he was letting himself in for. It all works out, and before I leave, I make sure to buy a few bottles of tasty stuff from the Cadenheads whisky shop just along the road from the distillery.

It has been a great way to end my whisky-connect in Scotland before moving over the Irish Sea to the Island of three legs and seven kingdoms. A blessed and cursed place full of light, shadows, and a crooked charm.

As the Steam Packet ferry grinds its way across a calm and rippling Irish Sea, I stand on the top deck of the *Ben My Chree* ferry and watch the sun go down over the west. It is stunning, both the sky and water are iridescent with all the colours of light and warmth. The golden globe above shimmers in all its intensity and I sense that this happening is a good omen. I feel a wave of emotion at the passing of one chapter of my life into another, and gently remove the watch from my left wrist. It has been there for many years, I have needed it for my job. Time has been my task-master. With the watch in my right hand, I look at the time for one last time. It is 20.35. and 15 seconds.

My attention lingers on the timepiece for a moment, and then I throw it as hard as I can out, and into the Irish Sea. It was not an expensive watch, and anyways, I don't need it any longer. Those days are done. Finished.

I breathe deeply the fresh salt-laden air laced with sea-spray and feel calm and content. Finally, as the colours fade in the presence of the oncoming night, I see the shape of the Island ahead, and watch streetlights twinkle like stars along the shoreline of Douglas Bay. This is my home now.

But I'm glad I am still handy for getting back to Scotland as and when I can.

I don't want to get too detached from whisky places and people.

Sometimes my mother is easy to care for, sometimes, she's not. I know how to care, but learn how to care more, understanding her foibles, her condition, her moods. Generally she's fine, as she has always been a positive person, and never stops appreciating the fact that I am there for her now. We go on trips, out in my van, she loves the van, where the views are better as the seat is higher than in a car. She loves the treats, the teas and scones, and ice creams, the fish and chips. She remains slim, whilst I get fatter. I join a gym.

Over time she gravitates further into her home, and wants to go out less, out into that noisy, turbulent world around her where people stare and then ignore her. Eventually, she remains in her bedroom as dementia makes a shrinking world smaller, and a small world is safer.

I have sorted out a bothy, just as soon as I arrived on the Island. I needed a studio for recording whisky reviews, and I needed a distraction from constant care duties. The old bothy, a nineteenth century servants stone hut is ideal. Small, rustic, well ventilated, a traditional single-room cavern where I can 'get away' and find some quiet for the perusal of whiskies, and other quality spirits, and for recording my videos for YouTube.

The channel grows steadily, slowly and steadily. Despite some attempts to get me deplatformed as a reviewer, I remain active and productive. There are several efforts by 'trolls' to get my channel cancelled as I am 'promoting a wrong message' but as of yet, they are still to succeed. I appreciate their efforts.

It keeps me on my toes and reminds me that ralfy has some haters. My channel will morph over time, adjusting as and when needed for growth. I am in no hurry, there's plenty of time. I have a lot more time these days. Wonderful, wonderful time. Time to do something, or, if I want, time to do nothing at all for a while. Time is such an undervalued resource to humanoids.

I have been an undertaker, so I know the higher value of time.

I cherish it.

My Patreon channel is growing steadily. I never ask much in subscription from the start, so as to encourage more subscribers, and the tactic works, backed up by increasingly regular content, moving from regular weekly additional videos to bi-monthly livestreams from the bothy. The bothy is a perfect place for a livestream. Rustic and isolated, I can be sure of not getting disturbed, and especially not getting pestered by whisky-grabbers. It is secure and hidden under mature trees out in the woodlands beyond where I live.

At night, as winter draws in again, I pour samples and assess my next batch of bottles shortlisted for review . . . and enjoy the silence. I prefer to drink alone. I drink a lot less than in company, and I taste a lot more of what I am sampling. A coal fire burns in the grate until I install a stove box, then a coal fire burns in that, with the occasional addition of peat blocks, which adds a lovely smell to the air, particularly when I am sipping Ardbeg, Lagavulin or Laphroaig.

Something I noticed at Glasgow's Whisky Club was too many people rushing their whiskies. The club was becoming habitual to them, and some were just drinking too much. Alcohol has that affect. Here in the bothy, I can pace it, and often I will place a lid on an unfinished glass and leave it 'till the following session in a few days. I can comfortably go a whole week without feeling the need to drink alcohol.

At one point, as my old mum becomes more troublesome due to prescribed, toxic medication, I am drinking too much beer, and develop a red nose of sorts. My brother comments, then I acknowledge it and I stop all alcohol for a month apart from review research and presentations. Once my mother has ceased ALL medically prescribed drugs, her health improves considerably, as does her mood. My suspicion of the medical profession has only ever grown stronger as life goes on. I see people die from 'cures' all the time. Most people are oblivious to their misplaced trust in professionals. It's the way humans are. The instincts for survival are weak when people are well-fed and happy to be gullible.

I look at many of the overpriced whisky bottlings on sale at the online shops. It's the same old, same old, wash, rinse, and repeat marketing strategies, persuading the faithful to part with valuable cash for hype and fashion. It's what some people want I suppose. To add insult to injury, tax in the form of V.A.T. is added to money already taken in the form of H.M.R.C. 'duty', so, in Britain, people pay tax on tax already being collected by the Bank of England.

Nobody ever seems to question this.

I sit in the Bothy and think about it, then wonder to myself about the wee man in the north who allegedly distils his own rum, for personal use only, and saves himself a fortune in not buying 'legal' liquor. I would love to try it, if I knew where to find him. He's famous for it. I should note though, that the wee man in the north is a known alcoholic with growing health problems and frequent bruises from fights with his son.

My old mother dies, during the night and at the age of 83, peacefully in her sleep, just at the point that she is beginning to show signs of suffering. I let her go without emotion. I have done all I can.

The funeral is a simple affair, no clergy, no fuss, no fake. My brother and I attend the committal at the local crematorium along with a friend. We scatter her ashes at a quiet spot near a small river, and out of the way of disturbance. I am very mindful of the fact that too many people I have helped in the past have had a lot worse situations than I have.

Some are scarred by regret.

Some just can't let go.

Some get stuck in the past, and are haunted by memories.

Some are angry, at others or at themselves, or at themselves and others too.

It is the human condition.

Thank goodness for whisky. A good whisky keeps you grounded in the real world and allows the enhanced mood of contemplation to provide explanation and comfort from darker thoughts. Half the problem is that humans have such a slanted, restricted view of the greater reality, that it's no wonder people get upset about death. Nobody seems to get upset about birth, but life and death in THIS reality are constant companions and totally inseparable. We all understand this better after a few whiskies.

Whisky helps so long as it is shown respect and not abused.

I just poured a bottle of cheap blended scotch into one of my barrels placed up on a worktop inside the bothy. It keeps the cask wet and leak-free and creates a dunnage warehouse feel to the place and makes it more whisky-specific. The ambient smell of liquor is beautiful. The dark mould of alcohol feeding fungi weave their way across the stone walls and give a more ambient look to the place.

I am alone now, my time is all mine, selfishly so, but it suits me to have the space to think bigger thoughts, and to make bigger plans for writing more books. I have written three now, and really appreciate the five star reviews from all those who have bought my first two books. This is my third book, a fictional autobiography about Life, Death & Whisky, as they all go so well together.

Death needs life.

Life needs death.

Both need whisky.

Whisky helps. This is why alcohol is found all across the universe in clouds of dust and liquor. Space clouds like Sagittarius B2, consist of silicon, water, and ethanol. It is huge, 3 million times larger than the mass of the sun. It spans light years of distance towards the centre of the Milky Way. If the alcohol was collected, it would taste of raspberry brulee. Ethyl formate is the ester responsible for the flavour of raspberry, and there's plenty of it in space.

I doubt I will ever get to taste Sagittarius B2, but no matter, I have some Signatory Mortlach to be getting on with along with a few other tasty malts and blends, and rums and mezcals and armagnacs and grappas and bourbons and ryes, and beers and wines and, well, lots and lots.

Chapter Fifteen – Bothy night

All the tasks of the day are done and it is now the later side of 8pm. A fire has been lit in the bothy and I am slightly tired from a busy day of whisky-business and other business. The air is cool, and the gathering night is fresh and clear.

There will be no rain 'till tomorrow.

I push the door across to block out the growing breeze, and take my seat by the stove where some coals and peat blocks smoulder together providing soft and ambient heat into the room. The casks loom across from me solid and passive in their purpose, helping to create the perfect environment for my malt-moments.

I will have a few this evening, and three bottles of highland whiskies are uncorked and waiting their turn for review assessment and appreciation. For such a moment, only good options are viable, with inferior bottles sitting far away on a shelf somewhere else.

It is bliss.

Time stands still.

There is no clock, no time-piece, no mobile devices, no way for the madding world to contact me and to spoil this precious moment. One single can of beer makes up the array. It will be all I need. I want to be non-sober, but not intoxicated . . . absolutely not drunk.

That would ruin the moment.

There is a point in the slow and methodical consumption of quality liquor that one can transcend mere intoxication and use the narcotic of alcohol to reach a higher level of perception. A state of alternative reality.

The philosophers over time have done it.

A condition of temporal ambient awareness, where time stands still and the mind is acute and articulate. One is tuned into the presence of the planet and of the universe beyond.

The situation cannot be rushed, and there comes a point that even one more sip of whisky will break the spell and end the moment.

175

With practice, like a shamanic ritual, a door on reality is opened, and we can get to see beyond.

It is precious and special.

After a while, I go outside for a pee and to smell the freshness of the air. I stand, paused and waiting for something, and then, carried on the wind sweeping up from the forest, I hear the distant clickety-click of the weaver making his cloth down within the trees somewhere. It is a beautiful moment. I would not be aware of it, but for the unsobered condition I have now reached from time in the bothy, dramming and listening to the silence by the fireside.

The sounds of weaving grow stronger again, carried on the wind which swishes softly through the shrubs and grass which surround the bothy. I listen again for more sounds of the loom, but it is gone. The memory remains, and like a seed, is growing within my imagination as a dimension of reality overlaps with another and demands I write a book, or perhaps three to find my way at last to the book of brilliant things.

I finish my whisky, lock the bothy door, and head off to bed, to sleep, deep and dreamless, all through the rest of the night 'till morning comes again.

It will be raining and cooler in the morning.

Summer is upon us, and winter is far away for now.

But the sun will never be far away. It never is.

Blessed is the sun.

Our dimension light of life.

Epilogue.

Life, Death & Whisky, what's it all about?
It's about living life as best we can.
It's about respecting, but not fearing death.
It's about understanding the value of time,
and what quality of life really, really is.
It's about being in the moment,
exploring the boundries of conciousness.
It's about whisky, good whisky,
with no time for bad whisky,
no time for pish.

Regards from ralfy 2022

Printed in Great Britain
by Amazon

15824315R00106